THE BEST of JUDGE DREDD

Published in 2013 by Prion Books
An imprint of the Carlton Publishing Group
20 Mortimer Street
London W1T 3JW

A CIP catalogue record for this book is available from the British Library

Editorial Manager: Roland Hall
Senior Art Editor: Stephen Cary
Designer: Elle Ward
Production: Claire Hayward

ISBN 978-1-85375-910-9

Printed in Dubai

CONTENTS

NATIONAL COMICS AWARD WINNER!
BEST CHARACTER – JUDGE DREDD
PROG 1345

A PROBLEM JUVE WHO CAN'T BE BEAT!
28p
FEATURING JUDGE DREDD

2000 AD
THE BIG WET
SUPERSURF 10 DOWN THE TUBES!

2000 AD
PROG 1348
BRIGHT LIGHTS, MEGA-CITY!

28p
FEATURING JUDGE DREDD
OH, HELL!

9 APR 1988
JUDGE DREDD

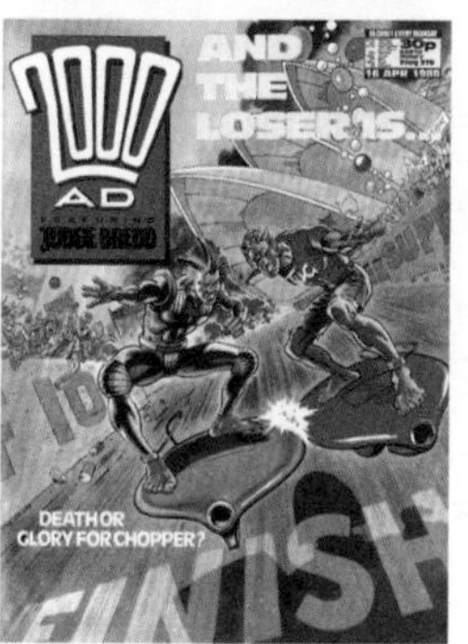

2000 AD
AND THE LOSER IS...
DEATH OR GLORY FOR CHOPPER?

JUDGE DREDD
SAVAGE
LOW LIFE
CHOPPER
2000 AD
LAND OF THE FREE?
DREDD DECLARES WAR ON TERROR

28p
FEATURING JUDGE DREDD
CRIMEWATCH 2110 AD
UNIVERSAL SOLDIER
AND MORE! MORE! MORE!

PROG 1561
STATE OF EMERGENCY
CAN DREDD FIND THE MANDROID BEFORE WAR IS DECLARED?

INTRODUCTION

BORAG THUNGG, EARTHLETS!

I am The Mighty Tharg, Betelgeusian editor of the award-winning SF anthology *2000 AD*, and I welcome you to a collection of some of the very best stories featuring future cop Judge Dredd!

Thirty-two years since his debut in Prog 2 of the Galaxy's Greatest Comic, and making an appearance in almost every single issue, Dredd has become the UK's most successful and iconic comics character. From the Judge's helmeted visage, the bizarreness of the streets he patrols in the nightmarish, violent twenty-second-century metropolis of Mega-City One, the hi-tech weaponry in the shape of his hulking Lawmaster bike and lethal Lawgiver pistol, or the strip's terrifying vision of a populace living in fear of a governing body with the powers of instant justice, it was immediately obvious that this was a series with the potential to be huge. And huge it was – Dredd quickly supplanted the rebooted Dan Dare as the readers' favourite, and cemented itself as the anthology's signature strip, capturing imaginations with the blizzard of ideas thrown into every story, enthralling with its action-packed tales, and blowing away the competition thanks to its gritty, dynamic artwork.

Dredd's extraordinary longevity can be attributed to the talent at the heart of the strip. Scripted in the main by John Wagner – working for a long period with writing partner Alan Grant – and with occasional input from Pat Mills, the stories were wonderfully crafted, full of drama, satire and black humour. Dredd's stoney-faced response to the many weird aliens, mutants, cyborgs and crazed perps that he encountered proved an enjoyable, drily witty contrast, taking the series to a new level of sophistication, unseen in children's comics at the time. And the artwork was sublime – the character has been brought to life by a stunning array of artists, such as original co-creator Carlos Ezquerra, Mike McMahon, Brian Bolland, Ian Gibson, Steve Dillon, Colin MacNeil and more, all adding depth and maturity to the strip with their vibrant pencils and inks.

Three decades later and Dredd continues to enforce the Law – both every week in *2000 AD* and every month in his own title, the *Judge Dredd Megazine* – and the character and his world continue to develop. Despite his many adventures, despite having defended the Big Meg from Sov invasion and zombie assault, from vengeance-seeking clone brothers and depraved Cursed Earth denizens, from rebellious robots and power-hungry madmen, there seems to be no stopping him. You can't keep a good lawman down.

I hope you enjoy this selection of classic Judge Dredd strips from the *2000 AD* archive, Earthlets – it would be a crime to miss them!

SPLUNDIG VUR THRIGG!

THARG

MEET the TOUGHEST LAWMAN of THEM ALL...
JUDGE DREDD
JUDGE
NEW YORK 2099 A.D.! WHERE HUGE STAR-SCRAPERS SOAR MILES INTO THE AIR! SMALL BUILDINGS LIKE THE EMPIRE STATE ARE IN RUINS... HIDE OUTS FOR VICIOUS CRIMINALS!
AT THE TOP OF THE EMPIRE STATE, CRIMINALS LOOK OUT AS A JUDGE RIDES ALONG THE ROAD TOWARDS THEM.
JUDGES ARE SPECIAL LAWMEN OF THE 21st. CENTURY. ELECTED BY THE PEOPLE TO ENFORCE THE LAW!
LOOK! A JUDGE! HE'S COMING TO ARREST US, WHITEY!
SHUT UP! WE'LL DEAL WITH HIM... JUDGES CAN BLEED, TOO!
POLICE CONTROL
2000 A.D.
NEW THRILL

THE CRIMINALS' LEADER WAS "WHITEY"
AND YOU'RE GONNA BLEED, JUDGE! I'M GONNA BLAST YOU WITH THIS **LASER CANNON**!
I HOPE IT'S **JUDGE DREDD** YOU BLAST, WHITEY—HE'S THE TOUGHEST OF THE JUDGES!

THE LASER BLAST RIPPED THE JUDGE OFF HIS BIKE.

THE CRIMINALS CLIMBED OUT OF THE EMPIRE STATE BUILDING.
HA, HA! YOU GOT HIM, WHITEY! YOU **WASTED** A JUDGE!
YEAH! AND IT WON'T BE THE LAST ONE I **FIX** EITHER!

DARN IT! IT'S JUDGE ALVIN—I WAS HOPING IT'D BE **DREDD**! NO SWEAT, THOUGH, **HIS TIME WILL COME**!
ALVIN
WHITEY PUT ON THE JUDGE'S HELMET.
LOOK AT ME, YOU PUNKS—I'M A JUDGE NOW! **JUDGE WHITEY**!
YEAH, WHITEY! THAT **JUDGE DREDD** AIN'T GOT **NOTHIN'** ON YOU!

MEANWHILE AT JUSTICE H.Q., THE GRAND JUDGE WAS TALKING TO **JUDGE DREDD**.
GOOD WORK, DREDD! SINCE YOU'VE BEEN PATROLLING SECTION SIX OF THE CITY CRIME HAS DROPPED DRAMATICALLY! THE PEOPLE ARE IN YOUR DEBT.
THANKS, YOUR HONOUR!

THE GRAND JUDGE SNARLED.

WHITEY'S ONE OF THOSE LAWBREAKERS HOLED UP IN THE OLD EMPIRE STATE! I'LL SEND IN AN AIR SQUAD TO BOMB THAT BUILDING AND EVERYONE IN IT OFF THE FACE OF THE EARTH!

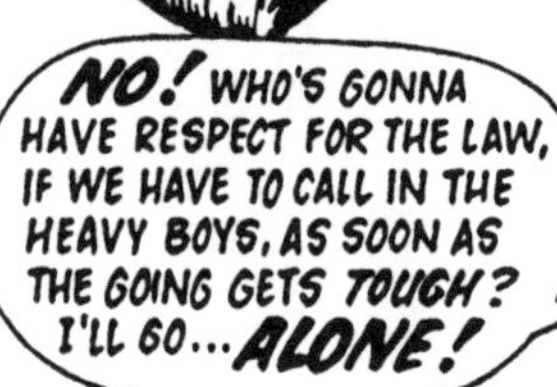

A FIGURE APPEARED BEHIND THEM.
LOOKING FOR ME, LAWBREAKERS? I SET MY BIKE ON AUTOMATIC, TOO!
JUDGE DREDD! YOU TRICKED US!
BLAST HIM, BOYS!
THE JUDGES ARE TRAINED TO HAVE LIGHTNING REACTIONS— DREDD'S GUN ROARED... ONCE!
TWICE!
DREDD
YOU COMMITTED THE MOST ODIOUS CRIME OF ALL, WHITEY- KILLING A JUDGE!
I'M GONNA PUT YOU AWAY FOR LIFE!
LATER.
NO PRISON CAN HOLD ME, DREDD! I'LL BUST OUT AND COME LOOKING FOR YOU! I HATE THE JUDGES AND ALL THEY STAND FOR!
THIS PRISON WILL HOLD YOU, WHITEY! WE'RE SENDING YOU TO... DEVIL'S ISLAND!

DEVIL'S ISLAND! A HUGE TRAFFIC ISLAND IN THE MIDDLE OF A VAST INTER-CITY HIGHWAY COMPLEX!
DEVIL'S ISLAND ONE WAY SPECIAL
NO— NOT DEVIL'S ISLAND! I'M SORRY! I'M SORRY!
250 LIMIT
YOU'LL HAVE ALL THE TIME IN THE WORLD TO REPENT YOUR ODIOUS OFFENCE, WHITEY... AS YOU LISTEN TO THE THUNDERING JUGGERNAUTS!
WHERE COMPUTER-CONTROLLED LORRIES ROAR PAST DAY AND NIGHT AT TWO HUNDRED MILES AN HOUR!
200 LIMIT
WHERE LAWBREAKERS WHO COMMIT SERIOUS CRIMES ARE MAROONED!
COME BACK, YOU RATS! COME BAAACK!
AIN'T NO ESCAPE FROM DEVIL'S ISLAND, MAN! THOSE TWO HUNDRED MILE AN HOUR MONSTERS NEVER STOP! YOU'RE HERE FOR LIFE—LIKE THE REST OF US! HEE, HEE!
BACK AT H.Q.
A STERN SENTENCE—BUT A NECESSARY ONE. THE PEOPLE MUST BE PROTECTED FROM VIOLENT LAWBREAKERS LIKE HIM, DREDD.
THEY DIED DEFENDING THE LAW
I'LL HANG UP JUDGE ALVIN'S BADGE WITH THE OTHERS.
SCANNER
SOMETIMES I THINK WE'RE ALL GOING TO DIE LIKE ALVIN, DREDD.
MAYBE, BUT IN MY BOOK, THAT'S THE ONLY WAY TO GO... IN DEFENCE OF THE LAW!
RIDE WITH THE JUDGE IN 2000 A.D. AGAIN, NEXT WEEK!

THE JUDGES, AMERICA'S LAWMEN OF THE 21st CENTURY, HAVE LITTLE SPARE TIME. GIVEN A FEW MINUTES TO RELAX YOU WOULD FIND JUDGE DREDD IN HIS APARTMENT, READING HIS LAW BOOKS. **HOWEVER...**

WHAT ARE SOUTH SEA ISLAND PALM TREES DOING IN THE MIDDLE OF MY APARTMENT?

LAW

MARIA—THE JUDGE'S ITALIAN CLEANING LADY ENTERED.

THIS IS MR. KEVIN O'NEILL!

I'M A SALESMAN FROM SENSOR-ROUND, JUDGE, SIR. WITH THIS SIMPLE CONTROL, YOU CAN PROJECT OUR DREAM WORLDS INTO YOUR ROOM...

TURN IT OFF!

2000 A.D.
Credit Card
SCRIPT ROBOT M. SHAW
ART ROBOT EZQUERRA
LETTERING ROBOT S. RICHARDSON

BUT, JUDGE—YOU NEVER HAVE NO *FUN*. A YOUNGA MAN LIKE YOU—HE SHOULD NOT WORK ALL DA TIME.

MARIA—THROW THIS ***FERRET-FACED PARASITE*** OUT BEFORE I DROWN YOU IN YOUR MINESTRONE!

JUDGE
JUDGE DREDD
YOU A-NEVER ENJOY YOURSELF, JUDGE. ALL-A YOU THINK OF IS LAW, LAW, LAW...
TO THINK I COULD GET A ROBOT-CLEANER FOR HALF THE PRICE AND SAVE ALL HER NAGGING!

THEN...
NOW WHAT? THIS IS SUPPOSED TO BE MY APARTMENT — NOT A SPACE SHUTTLE STATION!
JUDGE—THERE'S BEEN A MURDER ON THE 200th FLOOR OF THIS APARTMENT BLOCK. IT'S THE PRESIDENT OF SENSOR-ROUND!
ON THE 200th FLOOR.
I'VE SEEN SOME MURDER VICTIMS— BUT THIS POOR SAP TAKES FIRST PRIZE— HE'S BEEN RIPPED APART... BY SOME KINDA MONSTER!
OVER THE NEXT FEW DAYS, TWO OTHER TOP EXECUTIVES OF SENSOR-ROUND MET STRANGE DEATHS.
TUESDAY... IN THE MANAGING DIRECTOR'S ROOF TOP GARDEN...
'KWIKKA-GROW' JUICE—TO HELP MY BEGONIAS GROW BIG AND STRONG!
WHAAAAH?
WEDNESDAY... IN THE PRIVATE SWIMMING POOL OF SENSOR-ROUNDS ACCOUNTANT...
NOOOOOOOOO
YOU LIKE MY LITTLE PET? HOW DOES IT GRAB YA? HA-HA!
THURSDAY... JUDGE DREDD WAS ON PATROL, WHEN...
POLICE CONTROL TO JUDGE DREDD. VOICE PRINT RECORDED AT SCENE OF LAST MURDER IDENTIFIED AS CURATOR OF MOVIE SPECIAL EFFECTS MUSEUM, PROCEED WITH ARREST.
OF COURSE! IN THE SPECIAL EFFECTS MUSEUM ARE THE ROBOT MONSTERS USED IN OLD MOVIES. THINGS ARE BEGINNING TO CLICK...

AT THE MUSEUM.
BLOOD! THESE ROBOT MONSTERS DID THE KILLING. I GOTTA FIND THAT CRAZY CURATOR!
YOU AIN'T GOT FAR TO LOOK, JUDGE!
O'NEILL! I THOUGHT YOU WERE A SENSOR-ROUND SALESMAN!
ONLY WHEN IT SUITS ME, JUDGE. I NEED AN EXCUSE FOR LUGGING HEAVY EQUIPMENT AROUND TO KILL THE EXECUTIVES OF SENSOR-ROUND... DO YOU LIKE MY SQUID, SHE'S PRETTY, ISN'T SHE?
I HATE SENSOR-ROUND BECAUSE THEY BRING STUPID DREAM WORLDS INTO PEOPLE'S APARTMENTS. NOBODY WANTS TO SEE MONSTER MOVIES ANYMORE. AND THESE LOVELY MONSTERS ARE LEFT HERE TO RUST. RUST!
BUT I'M GOING TO CHANGE PEOPLE'S MINDS. OH, YES! I'M GOING TO GIVE THEM A MARVELLOUS MONSTER—
HOLD IT, O'NEILL!
SECONDS LATER, O'NEILL HAD ACTIVATED A MONSTER GORILLA...
KRONG! THE GREATEST FILM MONSTER EVER MADE!
I'VE PROGRAMMED HIM TO SMASH THE SENSOR-ROUND OFFICE-BUILDING INTO DUST!

HE'S RIPPING UP ROADWAYS—AND MY BULLETS JUST BOUNCE OFF!
GOTTA GET AFTER HIM.
HE'S ALREADY HALFWAY UP THE SENSOR-ROUND BUILDING—TEARING IT TO BITS. I'LL TAKE THE SPIRAL ROAD TO THE TOP...
FAST!
MY BIKE CANNON'S HARDLY MARKING HIM. THERE'S ONLY ONE OTHER WAY...

... GOTTA AIM MY BIKE AT THE GORILLA'S GULLET, AND PRAY THAT IT'LL...
... EXPLODE!
O'NEILL LOOKED UP, AS-
NO!
EZQUERRA
MY BEAUTIFUL KRONG — HIS HEAD'S GONE AND HE'S FALLING — ON ME... AT LEAST CHOKE WE'LL DIE, TOGETHER!
ALL YOUR DREAMS WERE CRUSHED, O'NEILL, BUT WITH DREAMS LIKE YOURS... WHO NEEDS NIGHTMARES?
AAAHHHHHHH

MEGA-CITY ONE, 2099. AT JUSTICE CENTRAL TOP LAWMAN JUDGE DREDD IS CATCHING UP WITH A BACKLOG OF CASE REPORTS...

I'M SORRY, SIR, YOU CAN'T GO IN THERE. THAT'S JUDGE DREDD'S PRIVATE OFFICE!

PUT A SOCK IN IT, SKINFACE! **DON UGGIE DON'T TAKE NO ORDERS FROM NOBODY!**

JUDGE DREDD

2000 A.D. Credit Card:
SCRIPT ROBOT JOHN WAGNER
ART ROBOT MIKE McMAHON
LETTERING ROBOT TONY JACOB
COMPU-73E

I ONLY GOT ONE TING TA SAY TA YA, DREDD - **NUTS!**

DON UGGIE APELINO AND HIS HENCHMEN, **FAST EEEK** AND **JOE BANANAS**. . . THE **APE GANG.**

UGGIE LEPT UP ONTO DREDD'S DESK.

DA **EAST SIDE MOB** IS MUSCLIN' IN ON OUR TERRITORY AN' YOU'RE TURNIN' A BLIND EYE. WELL, I WANNIT STOPPED OR **DERE'S GONNA BE TROUBLE**, SEE!

YOU TELL 'IM, DON UGGIE! DESE SKINFACE CREEPS MUST T'INK WE JUS' COME DOWN FROM DA **TREES** OR SOMETHIN'!

AS FAR AS I'M CONCERNED YOU AND THE EAST SIDE MOB ARE JUST THE SAME - **CHEAP HYPER-HOODS**. ONE STEP OUT OF LINE AND I'LL COME DOWN ON YOU **HARD**.

WHEN THE APE-HOODS HAD GONE, DREDD PONDERED THE PROBLEM. AFTER THE **GREAT HOLOCAUST** ONLY ZOO ANIMALS SURVIVED. AS TIME PASSED IT BECAME POSSIBLE TO **ALTER THE BRAIN-CELLS** OF APES, AND GIVE THEM THE ABILITY TO SPEAK.

SO DAT'S DA WAY IT IS, EH? WELL, YOU MARK MY WOIDS - DEM EAST SIDE PUNKS MESS WIT' DON UGGIE AN' DEY GET A **ONE-WAY RIDE TO DA MORGUE!**

YEAH! **DA STREETS IS GONNA BE RUNNIN' RED** - AN' IT AIN'T GONNA BE WIT' KETCHUP!

THEN ONE BY ONE THEY WERE ALLOWED FREEDOM...

APES ARE GREAT MIMICS. IT WAS ONLY TO BE EXPECTED THAT SOME OF THEM WOULD IMITATE CRIMINALS.

ZOO

KEEPER 172

DAYS LATER MEGA-CITY WAS ROCKED BY A GANG WAR, WHICH BEGAN WHEN DON UGGIE'S HOODLUMS RAIDED AN EAST SIDE MOB NIGHT CLUB . . .
GIVE IT DA WOIKS, BOYS!
TRY DA REFRESHIN' TASTE OF A HAIR 'N' KNUCKLE SANDWICH, SKINFACE!

THERE FOLLOWED AN ATTACK ON AN APE GANG GARAGE, THE GRUNT BROTHERS' SWINGING DAYS WERE OVER...
GRUNT!
GRUNT!
GUS'S GARAGE

THE APE GANG STRUCK BACK HARD. SONNY COSMO, NUMBER TWO IN THE EAST SIDE MOB, GOT A NEW PAIR OF BOOTS . . .
DAT'S A REAL NICE FIT, SONNY. AN' CON-CRETE TAKES A GOOD SHINE, TOO!
NO, NO!
PITY NO ONE'S GONNA SEE THEM WHERE YOU'RE GOIN'!
EEK! EEK!

ON THE FOURTH DAY OF THE GANGLAND WAR, DREDD DROVE INTO THE DISTRICT WHERE ALL THE FREED HAD SETTLED: THE JUNGLE!
BANANA BRUNCH
RUN-DOWN HOUSES, GARBAGE EVERYWHERE. APES HAVE FILTHY HABITS.
NOTHING WILL EVER CLEAN UP THE JUNGLE- BUT CLEANING UP DON UGGIE'S HOODLUMS WOULD SURE MAKE THE PLACE SMELL A LOT SWEETER.
WITH DIFFICULTY, DREDD CLIMBED THE APE STAIRCASE.
EVERYONE'S AFRAID TO GIVE EVIDENCE AGAINST THE GANGS, BUT WE'VE GOT TO CATCH THEM RED-HANDED... AND THE ONE APE THAT CAN HELP US LIVES UP THERE.
MAMA APELINO- DON UGGIE'S MOTHER.
AND SO...
YOU KNOW UGGIE'S A VICIOUS HOODLUM, MAMA - AND YOU'RE GOING TO GIVE ME SOME INFORMATION ON HIM...
WHAT YOU TALKIN' ABOUT, JUDGE? MY UGGIE, HE A GOOD APE. HE NO DO THE BAD THINGS YOU SAY.
DREDD
ACTING ON MAMA APELINO'S INFORMATION THE JUDGES INTERCEPT AN EAST SIDE MOB CONVOY CARRYING ILLEGAL TOBACCO INTO THE CITY...
JUDGES!
IT'S A HEIST, DROKK IT!
PULL OVER, LAWBREAKER!
75
TEN FOUR GOOD BUDDY
AAAGH!

DREDD BURST INTO THE CAB OF THE LEADING VEHICLE. . .
PULL OVER, I SAID!
THE CONVOY WAS SOON OVERPOWERED. . .
TAKE THEM DOWNTOWN AND BOOK THEM.
THE REST OF YOU GET INTO YOUR PLACES. WE'VE STILL GOT THE APE GANG TO DEAL WITH.

SOON, IN AN EMPTY WAREHOUSE ON THE EAST SIDE . . .
HERE DEY COME, BOSS!
OKAY, YOUSE APES-YOU KNOW DA PLAN. WE LET DEM SKINFACE PUNKS DRIVE IN AN' DEN WE PUT 'EM TO SLEEP WIT' DESE TOMMY GUNS.
WHAT DA HECK? DEM CREEPS IS SPEEDIN' UP!

EEEK!
CRASH!
GRUNT!

FREEZE, YOU APE-HOODS!
IT'S DA HEAT! WHACK 'EM OUT!

GET 'EM-UGGH!
GRUNT!
NO, MORE MONKEY BUSINESS FOR YOU, FAST EEEEK!
BUT, AS THE JUDGES GAINED THE UPPER HAND . . .
LOOK, JUDGE DREDD - DON UGGIE'S TRYING TO MAKE A BREAK FOR IT ALONG THE LIFTING CHAINS!
DREDD FIRED HIS LAWGIVER PISTOL, AND . . .
GRUNT! HELP-I'M FALLING!
LUCKILY, UGGIE LANDED ON HIS FEET . . .
YOUR DAYS OF CRIME ARE OVER, APE.
DAT'S WHERE YOU'RE WRONG, DREDD. YOUR CRIMINAL LAWS ONLY COVER HUMANS - DEY DON'T SAY NUTTIN' ABOUT APES! YA CAN'T TOUCH ME!
THERE IS ONE LAW. MAYBE YOU SECOND GENERATION FREE APES DON'T REMEMBER IT. BUT YOUR MAMA DID . . .
. . . AND THANKS TO HER I'M GOING TO PUT YOU WHERE YOU BELONG . . . BEHIND BARS.

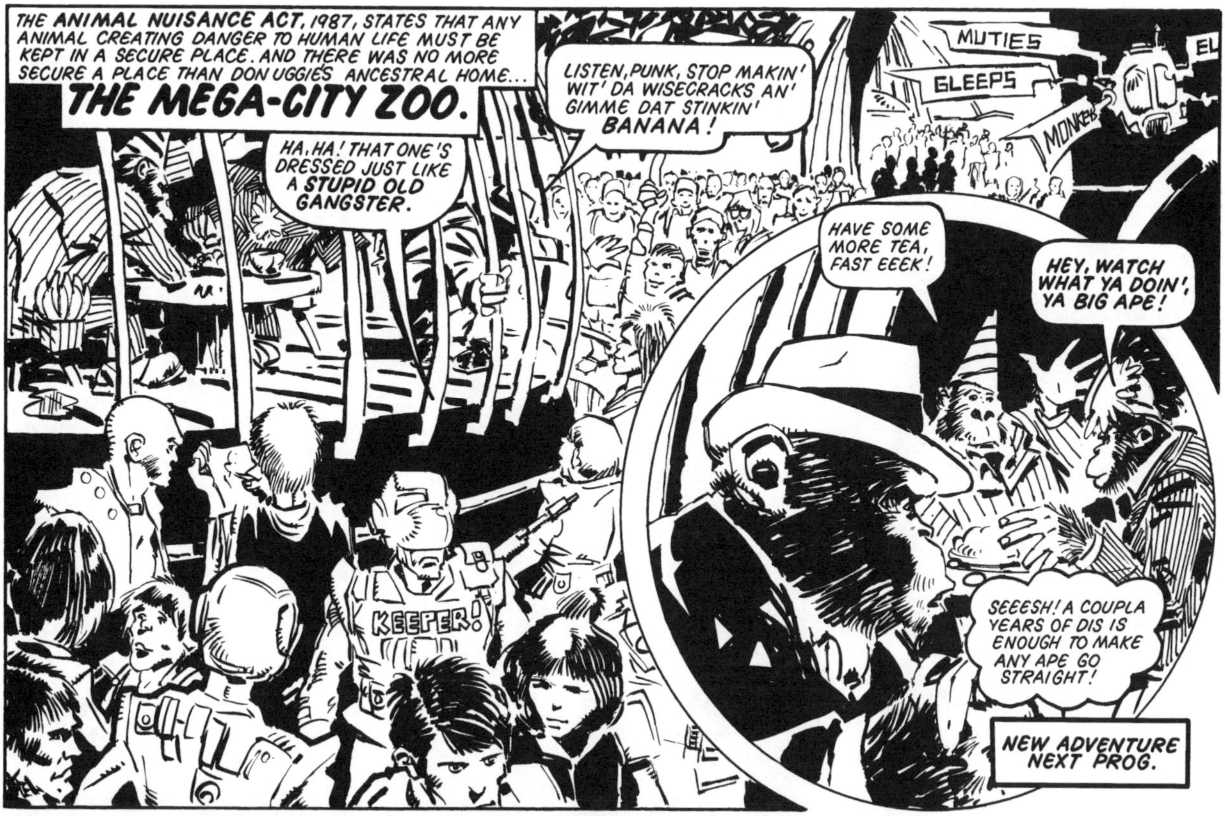

THE ANIMAL NUISANCE ACT, 1987, STATES THAT ANY ANIMAL CREATING DANGER TO HUMAN LIFE MUST BE KEPT IN A SECURE PLACE. AND THERE WAS NO MORE SECURE A PLACE THAN DON UGGIE'S ANCESTRAL HOME...
THE MEGA-CITY ZOO.

HA, HA! THAT ONE'S DRESSED JUST LIKE A **STUPID OLD GANGSTER.**

LISTEN, PUNK, STOP MAKIN' WIT' DA WISECRACKS AN' GIMME DAT STINKIN' **BANANA!**

MUTIES

GLEEPS

MONKEYS

KEEPER!

HAVE SOME MORE TEA, FAST EEEK!

HEY, WATCH WHAT YA DOIN', YA BIG APE!

SEEESH! A COUPLA YEARS OF DIS IS ENOUGH TO MAKE ANY APE GO STRAIGHT!

NEW ADVENTURE NEXT PROG.

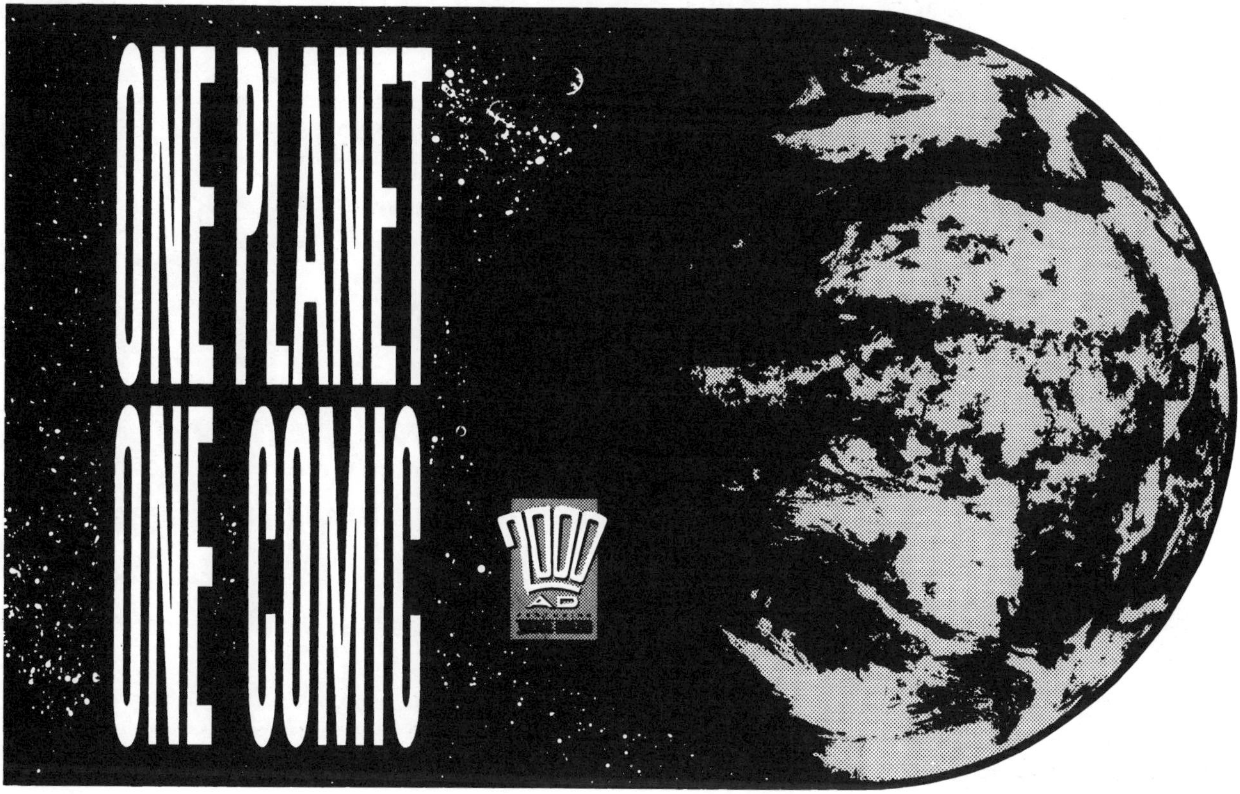

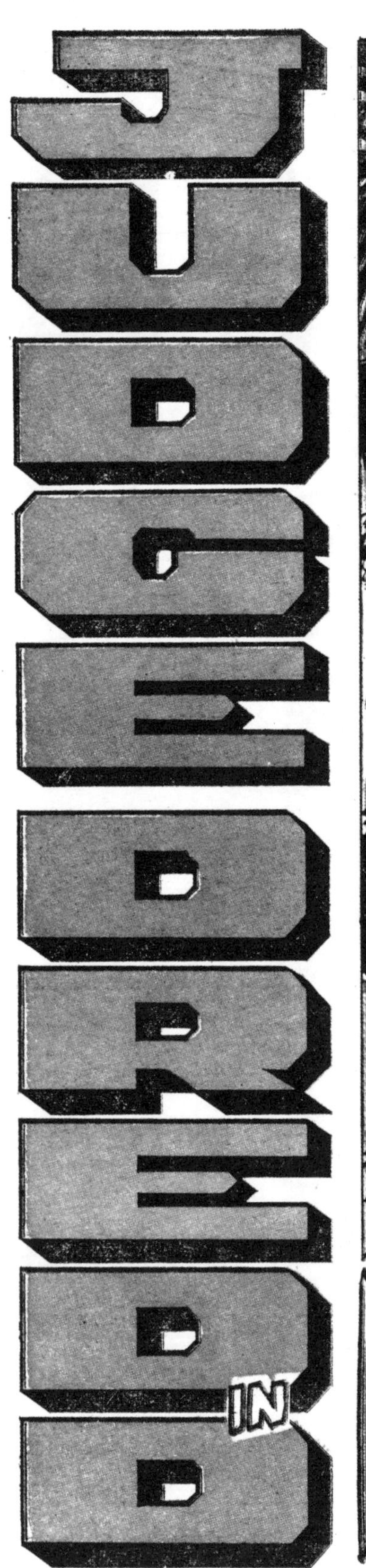

FIREBUG

FIRE!

LEAP FOR YOUR LIVES!

FIRE WAS A DEADLY DANGER IN MEGA-CITY 1. FROM THE MILE-HIGH STRATOSCRAPERS THERE WAS ONLY ONE ESCAPE —

GLIDE CHUTE!

LEVEL 65

THE FIREBUG HAS STRUCK AGAIN!

AAAAGH!
BE CAREFUL, YOU FOOL! WHERE WERE YOU DURING GLIDE CHUTE PRACTICE?
2000 A.D.
Credit Card:
SCRIPT ROBOT JOHN HOWARD
ART ROBOT MIKE McMAHON
LETTERING ROBOT TOM FRAME
COMPU-73E

CONTROLLING THE RESCUE OPERATION, MEGA-CITY'S TOP LAWMAN, JUDGE DREDD...
LOOK OUT, YOU PEOPLE! - FLAMER COMING DOWN!
AIEEEE!
GET SOME FOAM ON THOSE PEOPLE — QUICK!
I'M JUDGE DWEDD'S WOBOT. PLEASE GIVE THESE SANDWICHES TO HIM. HE MUST KEEP HIS STWENGTH UP!
IT WAS LATE INTO THE NIGHT BEFORE THE FIRE WAS BROUGHT UNDER CONTROL. BY THEN, HUNDREDS HAD DIED...
IT'S THE WORK OF THE FIREBUG FOR SURE, DREDD. HIS TENTH... MMM, DELICIOUS SANDWICHES... I'M RELYING ON YOU TO FIND HIM BEFORE HE HAS THE WHOLE CITY IN ASHES!
THERE ARE 800 MILLION PEOPLE IN THIS CITY, CHIEF JUDGE. FINDING ONE NUT WHO GETS HIS KICKS OUT OF STARTING FIRES IS LIKE LOOKING FOR A NEEDLE IN A HAYSTACK.
DREDD RETURNED TO HIS APARTMENT, BUT HIS SLEEP WAS FITFUL...
FIREBUG... ONE MANIAC LOOSE IN THE CITY... BUT WHO... WHO?
DREDD'S ROBOSERVANT WALTER WOKE HIS LAWMAN AT 7 AM...
GOOD MORNING, JUDGE DWEDD. TODAY IS THE ANNIVERSARY OF THE DAY WALTER WON HIS FWEEDOM PAPERS, AND WALTER HAS A SUPWISE FOR YOU —
EH...? WHAT THE HECK IS THIS?

AS A TOKEN OF WALTER'S LOVE AND WESPECT FOR YOU, WALTER HAS BURNT HIS FWEEDOM PAPERS AND HAD THESE DEEDS DWAWN UP.
YOU NOW OWN WALTER — LOCK, STOCK AND CIRCUITS!
OWNERSHIP DEEDS! DROKK IT! YOU STUPID ROBOT!
DEED OF OWNERSHIP
WALTER

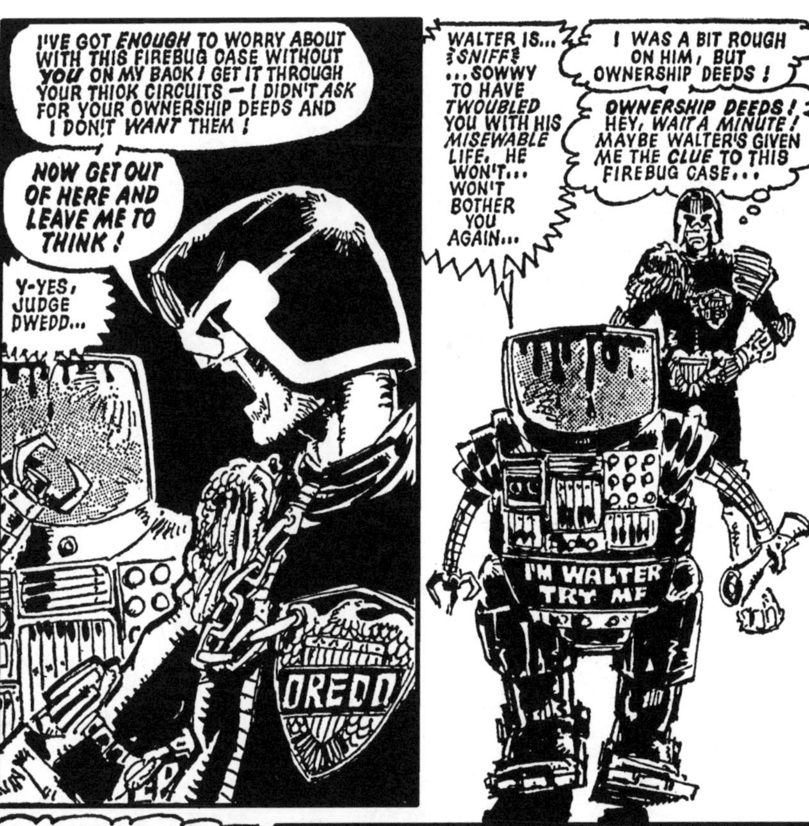
I'VE GOT ENOUGH TO WORRY ABOUT WITH THIS FIREBUG CASE WITHOUT YOU ON MY BACK! GET IT THROUGH YOUR THICK CIRCUITS — I DIDN'T ASK FOR YOUR OWNERSHIP DEEDS AND I DON'T WANT THEM!
NOW GET OUT OF HERE AND LEAVE ME TO THINK!
Y-YES, JUDGE DWEDD...
DREDD
WALTER IS... *SNIFF* ...SOWWY TO HAVE TWOUBLED YOU WITH HIS MISEWABLE LIFE. HE WON'T... WON'T BOTHER YOU AGAIN...
I WAS A BIT ROUGH ON HIM, BUT OWNERSHIP DEEDS!
OWNERSHIP DEEDS! HEY, WAIT A MINUTE! MAYBE WALTER'S GIVEN ME THE CLUE TO THIS FIREBUG CASE...
I'M WALTER TRY ME

MAYBE THIS FIREBUG ISN'T A RANDOM NUT — MAYBE...
DREDD TO CONTROL... GET ONTO PUBLIC RECORDS OFFICE AND SEE WHO OWNS THE DEEDS TO THE FIREBUG PROPERTIES. I'M COMING IN!
THE CHIEF JUDGE WAS WAITING FOR DREDD AT JUSTICE CENTRAL...
YOU'VE STRUCK PAYDIRT, DREDD. THE BUILDINGS ALL BELONG TO A MR CHUCK McCRACKEN. HE'S BEEN IN FINANCIAL TROUBLE LATELY — THE INSURANCE MONEY WOULD GET HIM OUT OF IT.
NOW ALL WE'VE GOT TO DO IS PROVE IT. I'LL HAVE McCRACKEN HAULED IN!

McCRACKEN WAS BROUGHT IN...
BEFORE YOU SAY ANYTHING, CITIZEN, LET ME SAY THAT I BELIEVE YOU SET FIRE TO YOUR OWN BUILDINGS IN ORDER TO COLLECT THE INSURANCE MONEY.
THAT MACHINE IN THERE WILL REMOVE THE TOP LAYER OF SKIN FROM YOUR ENTIRE BODY. WE'RE GOING TO TEST IT FOR TRACES OF FIRE-RAISING CHEMICALS.

THAT'S RIDICULOUS!
YOU - YOU CAN'T DO THIS TO ME!
I CAN AND I WILL — UNDER THE AUTHORITY GRANTED TO ME BY THE "REASONABLE GROUNDS FOR SUSPICION" ACT OF 2086 TAKE HIM AWAY!
AARGH!
STOP SCREAMING — WE HAVEN'T EVEN TOUCHED YOU — YET!
THE PROCESS ONLY LASTED MINUTES. SOON...
WE GOT HIM COLD. ANALYSIS OF THE SKIN SHOWS TRACES OF A PETROL BASED FIRE-RAISER.
CHARLES Q McCRACKEN, I FIND YOU GUILTY ON TEN COUNTS OF ARSON AND 718 COUNTS OF HOMICIDE. HAVE YOU ANYTHING TO SAY ?
SHEESH!
I THOUGHT NOT, TAKE HIM AWAY!
GOOD WORK, DREDD. TAKE THE REST OF THE DAY OFF YOU'VE GOT A LOT OF SLEEP TO CATCH UP ON.
DREDD

THE WEARY LAWMAN RETURNED TO HIS APARTMENT...
WALTER, I'M HOME! WALTER! NOW WHERE THE HECK...HMMM... NOTE ON THE TABLE...
Dear Judge Dwedd —
IF Walter cannot be your -Wobot, there is no weason for him to go on living. Walter has decided to find a tall building and thwow himself off.
This humble wobot is gwateful for the few, bwief, pwecious moments you allowed him to spend with you.
Yours always,
Walter xxx
P.S. There is some nice cold tweacle pudding in the Fwidge.
OH, DROKK!

DREDD PUT OUT AN IMMEDIATE CALL TO THE EMERGENCY SERVICES—
CLIMB ABOARD, JUDGE. ONE OF OUR PATROLS HAS SPOTTED A ROBOT ON THE WENGLER BUILDING.
POLICE

SOON, NOT FAR AWAY...
GOODBYE, CWUEL WORLD!
THERE HE IS!

WALTER! STOP! I DIDN'T MEAN TO BE SO ROUGH!
JUDGE DWEDD! YOU-YOU MEAN YOU... O-OH CWIPES, THE BIKE!

GOODBYE, JUDGE DWEDD! WALTER LOVE YOU!
GET THE NET OUT– FAST!
I'M WALTER TRY ME
THE HOVERBUS MADE IT – JUST IN TIME!
CRANG!
CLANG!
SOME DAMAGE THERE, JUDGE. WE'D BETTER GET HIM TO THE ROBOCLINIC.
TWO HOURS LATER, DREDD CALLED AT THE ROBOCLINIC...
H-HELLO, JUDGE DWEDD. WALTER IS VEWY SOWWY FOR ALL THE TWOUBLE HE HAS CAUSED YOU.
AND SO YOU SHOULD BE! NO ROBOT OF MINE IS GOING TO BEHAVE IN THAT RIDICULOUS MANNER AGAIN!
W-WOBOT OF YOURS? YOU... YOU MEAN?
THAT'S RIGHT. I'M FILING THESE DEEDS OF OWNERSHIP TODAY. THE NEXT TIME YOU STEP OUT OF LINE IT'LL BE THE ROBOT AUCTIONS FOR YOU!
OH, JUDGE DWEDD! YOU'VE MADE WALTER THE HAPPIEST WOBOT IN THE WORLD!
NEXT PROG:
THE CURSED EARTH!

12 APR 80
PROG 160
AND TORNADO
Malaysia $1.00
New Zealand 35c
Australia 35c
South Africa 35c
Mercury 17g
Venus 10g
Mars 15g
Asteroid Belt 20g
Saturn 84g
Neptune 87g
Pluto 93g
12p
EARTH MONEY
IN ORBIT EVERY MONDAY
SHALL I TELL THEM, PA ?
NO, LET ME !
I'LL DO IT, PA !
JUDGE DREDD IS A DEAD MAN !
DREDD HITS TEXAS CITY — AND TEXAS CITY HITS BACK !

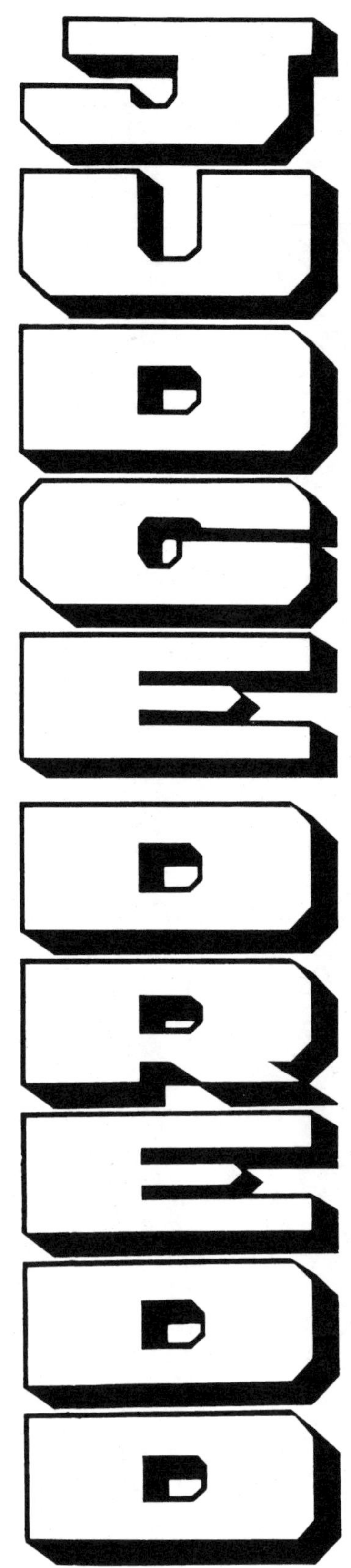

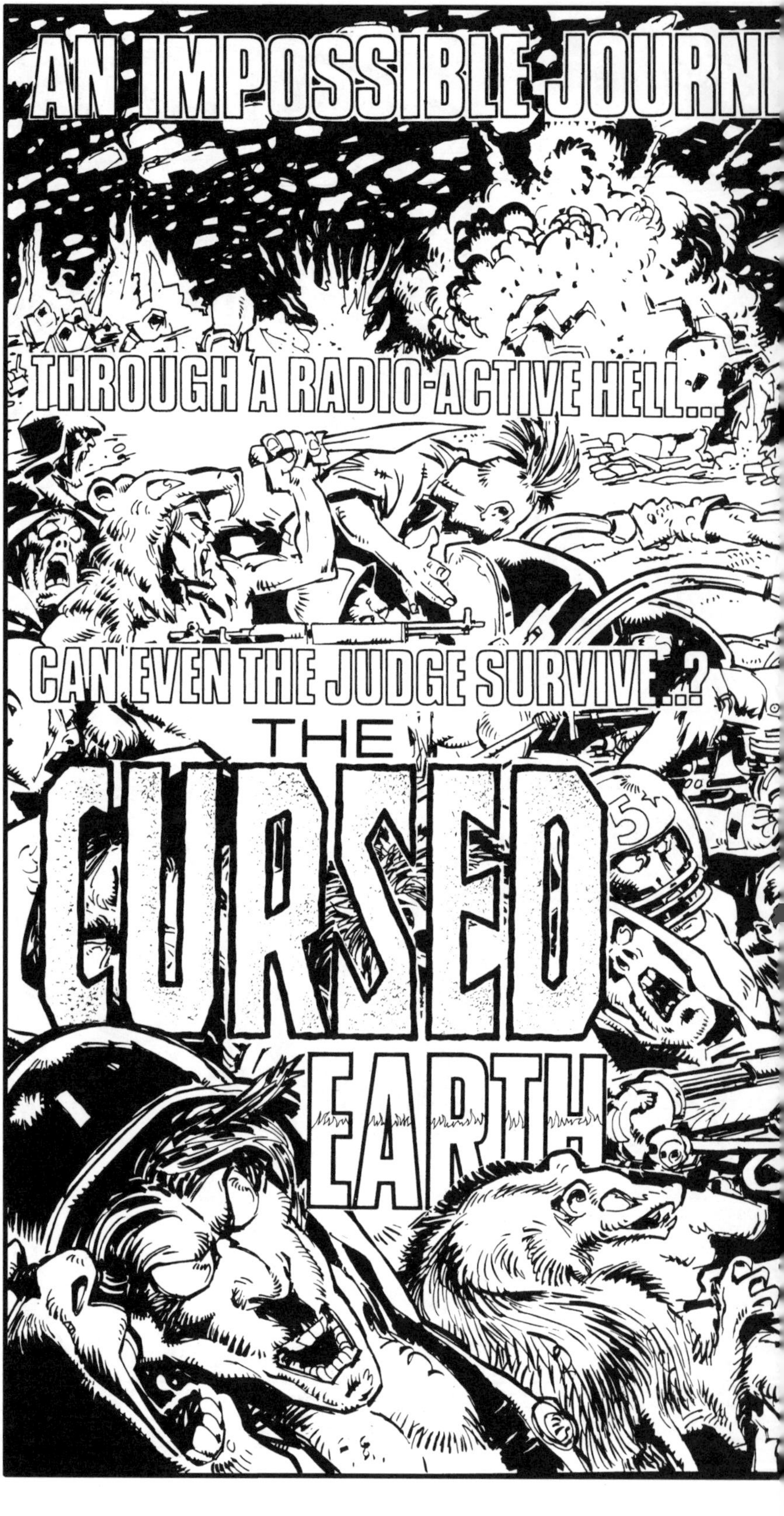

AN IMPOSSIBLE JOURN

THROUGH A RADIO-ACTIVE HELL...

CAN EVEN THE JUDGE SURVIVE..?

THE CURSED EARTH

2000 A.D.
Credit Card:
SCRIPT ROBOT
PAT MILLS
ART ROBOT
MIKE McMAHON
LETTERING ROBOT
TOM FRAME
COMPU-73E
NEVER A DULL MOMENT WHEN YOU'RE A TWENTY-SECOND CENTURY COP!

CHAPTER ONE :

FORBIDDEN FRUIT!

SPECIAL SECURITY WING, JUSTICE H.Q., MEGA-CITY ONE. **JUDGE DREDD** IS CALLED OFF PATROL TO MEET AN OLD FRIEND...

HELLO, RED. LONG TIME – NO SEE. HEAR YOU GOT A ***HELLUVA*** STORY TO TELL ME.

HELL IS THE RIGHT WORD, JUDGE...

FOOD STERILE UNIT

QUAR-BUB 55

IN CHARGE OF THE WING – ASSISTANT GRAND JUDGE FODDER...

YOU'LL HAVE TO EXCUSE RED BEING INSIDE THE ***PLASTIC BUBBLE***, JUDGE. HIS PERIOD OF *QUARANTINE* IS NOT YET UP.

BUT HE HAS EVERY COMFORT... *MUSIC...TV...*

CAN WE GET ON WITH IT ? IN THE TIME I'VE WASTED WITH YOU, JUDGE FODDER, I COULD HAVE ARRESTED ***FIVE LAW-BREAKERS!***

SORRY, JUDGE DREDD. I KNOW YOU'RE A BUSY MAN. GO AHEAD, RED. GO AHEAD.

HOLOGRAM CORP

OKAY... WELL, AS YOU KNOW, I'M A STRATO-PILOT. I FLY THE SHORT HAUL PLANES BETWEEN *MEGA-CITY ONE* AND *MEGA-CITY TWO* ON THE WEST COAST...

IT WAS A NICE EASY RUN, JUDGE... THEN... ***THEN*** THE ***PLAGUE*** CAME TO MEGA-CITY TWO... PEOPLE ***DYING*** IN THEIR THOUSANDS...

...ME AND MY MEN WERE TO DELIVER THE VACCINE...THE ***ONLY*** *THING THAT COULD SAVE THE REST OF THE WORLD FROM A* ***TERRIBLE FATE!***

TAKE IT EASY, RED... JUST TELL IT IN YOUR OWN WAY...

"IT WAS JUST TWO WEEKS AGO AS WE HEADED TOWARDS MEGA-CITY TWO... FLYING OVER THE CURSED EARTH, THE STRETCH OF SMOULDERING WASTELAND BETWEEN THE MEGA CITIES... LEFT OVER FROM THE ATOMIC WAR..."
STRAT BAT
GEE, RED... SURE LOOKS LIKE HELL DOWN THERE... FIVE HUNDRED MILE AN HOUR WINDS, MONSTERS AND SAVAGE MUTIES...
YEAH... NOTHING GROWS IN THAT DESERT... THE DEATH BELT ONE MILE UP SEES TO THAT...!
I'M SURE GLAD WE'RE FLYING ABOVE IT... IMAGINE TRYING TO CROSS IT ON THE GROUND. IT WOULD BE SUICIDE!
WE SHOULD BE APPROACHING THE HOLE IN THE DEATH BELT ABOVE MEGA-CITY TWO — IN THREE MINUTES...
MEGA-CITY TWO... COVERING FIVE THOUSAND SQUARE MILES OF THE CALIFORNIAN WEST COAST...AND, ALONG WITH MEGA-CITY ONE AND MEGA-CITY THREE, THE ONLY PLACES OF CIVILISATION LEFT IN AMERICA...
THERE IT IS! HEY, WHAT EXACTLY IS THIS PLAGUE, RED?
A DISEASE LEFT OVER FROM THE GREAT GERM WAR. YOU KNOW... THE ONE THAT CAME AFTER THE ATOMIC WAR. SOMEHOW IT GOT INTO THE CITY...
...IT TURNS PEOPLE'S SKIN GREY AND SCRAMBLES THEIR BRAINS BEFORE THEY DIE...
NINE SHUTTLE STOP
CONAPT 573 SECTOR NINE
McMahon '77

LUCKILY, WE'RE IN TIME TO HELP. WE GOT THE VACCINE ON BOARD THAT WILL CURE THEM... AFTER ALL, WE MEGA-CITIES HAVE GOT TO STICK TOGETHER. WE'RE ALL THAT'S LEFT...
PAO 26
HEY... THAT'S FUNNY... THE AIRPORT'S DESERTED...
ANYBODY AROUND...?
I DON'T LIKE IT, RED...
ME NEITHER... LISTEN... CAN YOU HEAR SOMETHING?
TOOTY FRUITY...
IT'S A SORTA... CHANTING! WHO'S THERE? IDENTIFY YOURSELVES!
TOOTY FRUITY!
PLAGUE MEN! LOOK OUT!
WAIT! IF - IF YOU HAVEN'T GONE TOO FAR, WE CAN HELP YOU! WE GOT THE VACCINE!
WE DO NOT WANT THE VACCINE... WE WANT. . . THE FORBIDDEN FRUIT!
DO NOT USE THE GUNS... IT SPOILS THE FRUIT WHEN YOU SPIT OUT THE BULLETS!
SECURITY 9

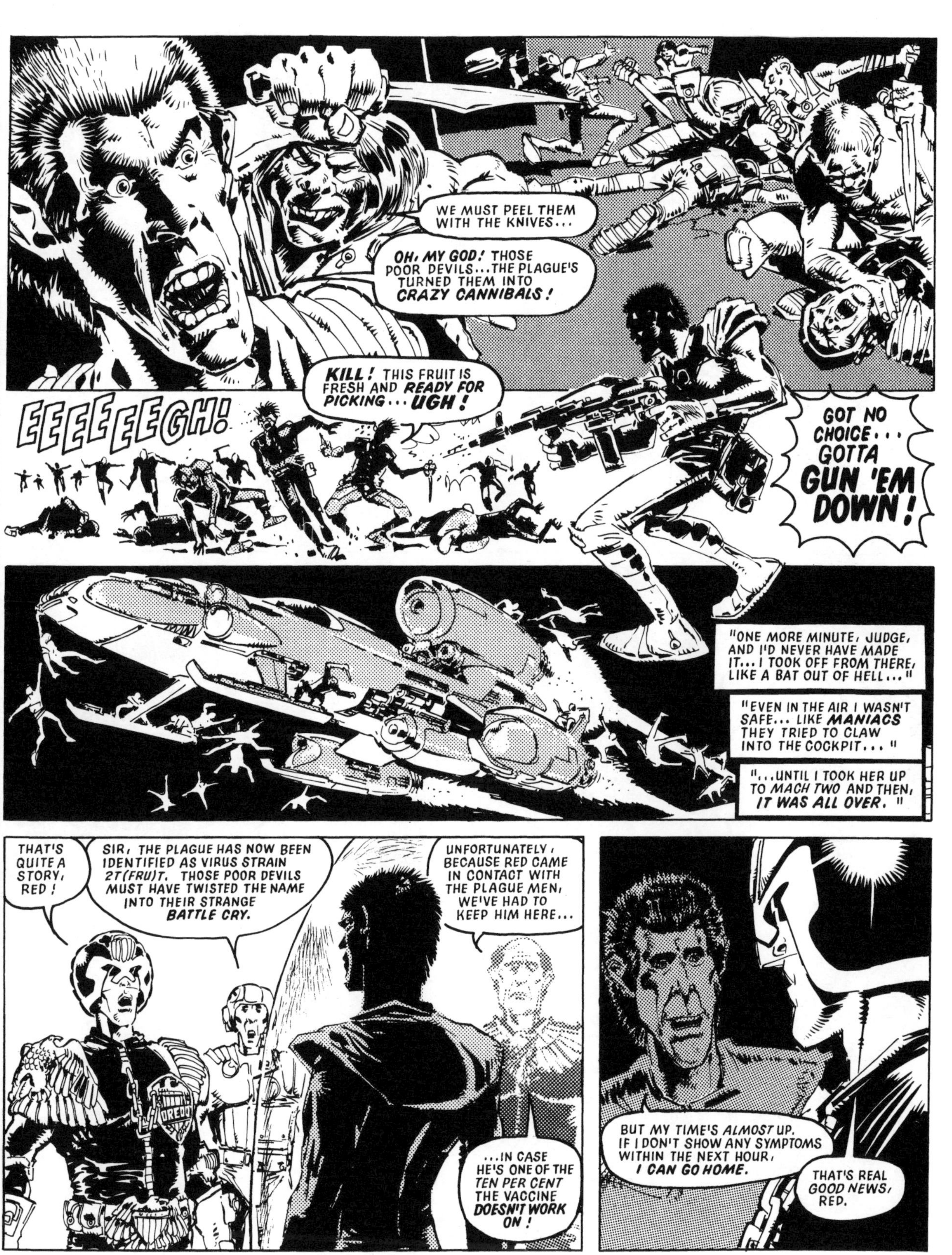

WE MUST PEEL THEM WITH THE KNIVES...

OH, MY GOD! THOSE POOR DEVILS... THE PLAGUE'S TURNED THEM INTO ***CRAZY CANNIBALS!***

KILL! THIS FRUIT IS FRESH AND ***READY FOR PICKING... UGH!***

EEEEEEGH!

GOT NO CHOICE... GOTTA GUN 'EM DOWN!

"ONE MORE MINUTE, JUDGE, AND I'D NEVER HAVE MADE IT... I TOOK OFF FROM THERE, LIKE A BAT OUT OF HELL..."

"EVEN IN THE AIR I WASN'T SAFE... LIKE ***MANIACS*** THEY TRIED TO CLAW INTO THE COCKPIT..."

"...UNTIL I TOOK HER UP TO *MACH TWO* AND THEN, ***IT WAS ALL OVER.***"

ONLY ONE SECTION OF MEGA-CITY TWO IS HOLDING OUT. IT DESPERATELY NEEDS THAT VACCINE.
WITH THE AIRPORTS IN THE PLAGUE MEN'S HANDS, THERE'S ONLY ONE OTHER WAY...
...BY LAND! AND THAT'S WHERE I COME IN, HUH?

FORGET IT! TO SURVIVE THE CURSED EARTH, A THOUSAND MILES OF MAN MADE HELL, I'D NEED SPECIAL MEN...A SPECIAL MACHINE...
WE GOT THEM, DREDD...IF YOU'LL DO IT...
HUUUH...? MY HANDS...? WHAT'S HAPPENING...?

TOOTY...?
YOUR SURVIVAL CHANCES ARE LOW...BUT IT'S GOT TO BE TRIED...
...FOR THE FUTURE OF CIVILISATION..!

...IS IN YOUR HANDS!
AAAGH!
TOOTY FRUITY!

HE'S STRANGLING HIM... HE'S TURNED INTO A PLAGUE MAN!
WANT... MUST HAVE... FORBIDDEN FRUIT!
HE-HE'S SHOVING THE ASSISTANT GRAND JUDGE THROUGH HIS FOOD STERILISATION CHAMBER!

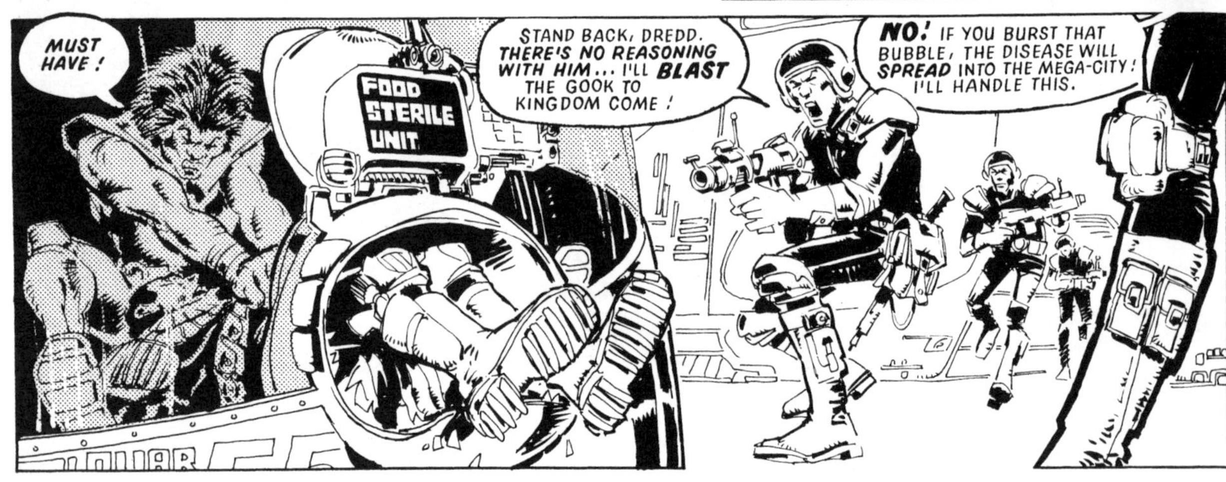
MUST HAVE!
FOOD STERILE UNIT
STAND BACK, DREDD. THERE'S NO REASONING WITH HIM... I'LL BLAST THE GOOK TO KINGDOM COME!
NO! IF YOU BURST THAT BUBBLE, THE DISEASE WILL SPREAD INTO THE MEGA-CITY! I'LL HANDLE THIS.

DROKK! THE BUBBLE'S PULLING MY PUNCHES!
RED NOT LIKE THAT, DREDD... RED MAKE YUM-YUM WITH YOU...!

...RED...WANT...YOUR JUICES!
RED... YOU GOTTA UNDERSTAND... I WANT TO HELP YOU...
UUHH!
OH, NO! HE'S GRABBING JUDGE FODDER'S GUN!
HA! RED BLAST HIS WAY OUT!
IF HE PULLS THAT TRIGGER, HE'LL BLOW HIMSELF AND HIS GERMS ALL OVER MEGA-CITY!

EVERY JUDGES' GUN HAS A SELF-DESTRUCT MECHANISM IF USED BY UNAUTHORISED PERSONS...
TOOTY FRUITY!
ONLY ONE CHANCE... THE T.V....

YOU HAD TO KILL THE PLAGUE MEN...AND NOW— I GOTTA KILL YOU!
I'M SORRY, OLD BUDDY — THERE'S NO OTHER WAY.
AAAGH!

HE'S DEAD! YOU JUST SAVED MEGA-CITY ONE, DREDD. NOW... WILL YOU SAVE MEGA-CITY TWO?
WHEN THOUSANDS COULD TURN INTO CRAZY MONSTERS LIKE RED...? THERE'S NO REFUSING!
I OWE HIM! ...SHOW ME MY WHEELS...I WANT TO GET MOVING... FAST!
SOMEHOW I'M GONNA MAKE IT — ACROSS THE CURSED EARTH!
DREDD
Next Prog: INTO THE DARKNESS!

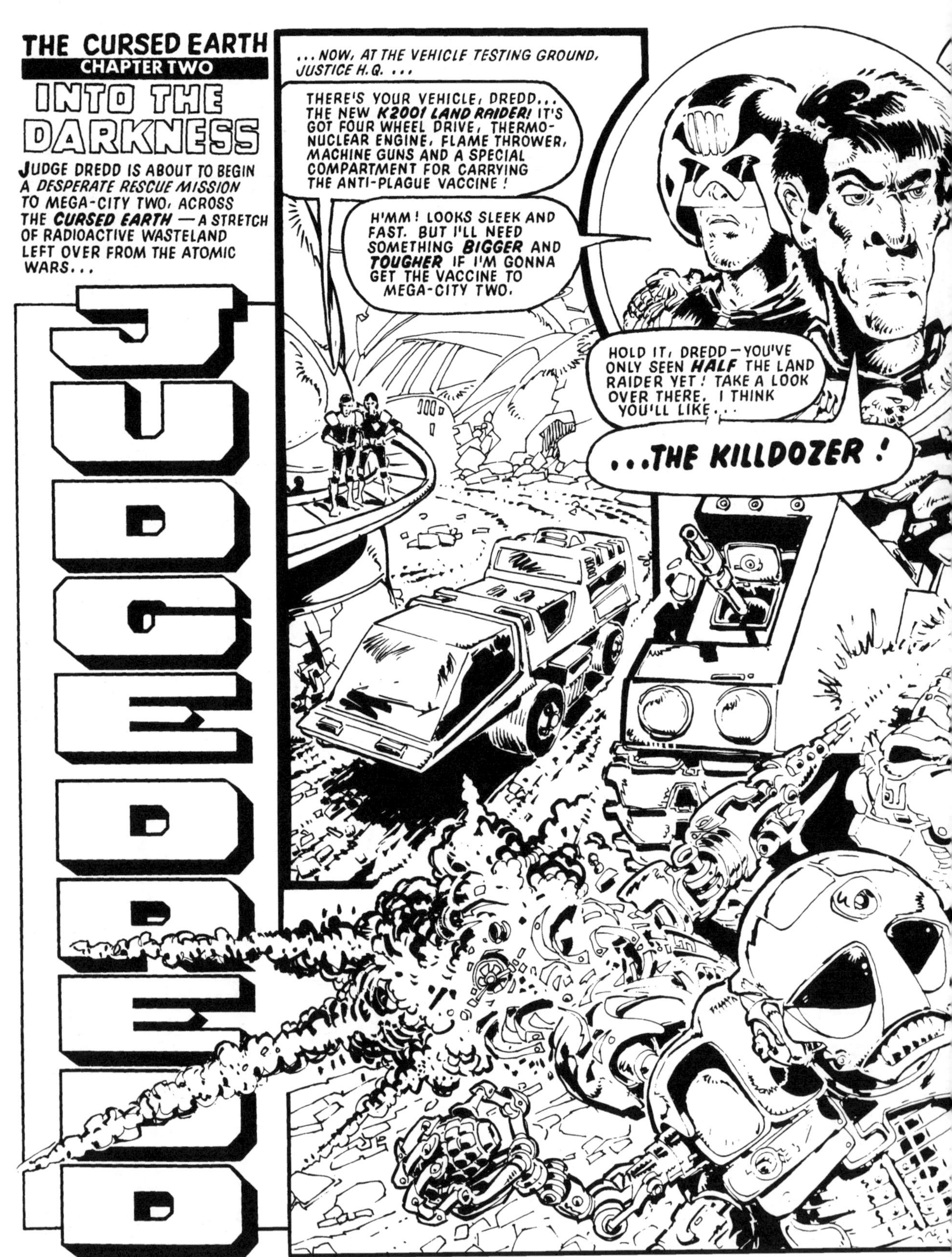
THE CURSED EARTH
CHAPTER TWO
INTO THE DARKNESS
JUDGE DREDD IS ABOUT TO BEGIN A DESPERATE RESCUE MISSION TO MEGA-CITY TWO, ACROSS THE CURSED EARTH — A STRETCH OF RADIOACTIVE WASTELAND LEFT OVER FROM THE ATOMIC WARS...
JUDGE DREDD
...NOW, AT THE VEHICLE TESTING GROUND, JUSTICE H.Q. ...
THERE'S YOUR VEHICLE, DREDD... THE NEW K2001 LAND RAIDER! IT'S GOT FOUR WHEEL DRIVE, THERMO-NUCLEAR ENGINE, FLAME THROWER, MACHINE GUNS AND A SPECIAL COMPARTMENT FOR CARRYING THE ANTI-PLAGUE VACCINE!
H'MM! LOOKS SLEEK AND FAST. BUT I'LL NEED SOMETHING BIGGER AND TOUGHER IF I'M GONNA GET THE VACCINE TO MEGA-CITY TWO.
HOLD IT, DREDD — YOU'VE ONLY SEEN HALF THE LAND RAIDER YET! TAKE A LOOK OVER THERE. I THINK YOU'LL LIKE...
...THE KILLDOZER!

2000 A.D. Credit Card:
SCRIPT ROBOT PAT MILLS
ART ROBOT MIKE McMAHON
LETTERING ROBOT TOM FRAME
COMPU-73E
THE KILLDOZER IS EQUIPPED WITH NEMESIS ROCKETS, CANNON, LASER GUNS, TWO NEW QUASAR BIKES, AND IS NUCLEAR BLAST-PROOF.
IT'S A MOBILE FORTRESS. IS THAT BIG AND TOUGH ENOUGH FOR YOU, DREDD?
IT'LL DO.
NOTHING IMPRESSES THE JUDGE.
THE KILLDOZER LINKS UP WITH THE LAND-RAIDER TO FORM A MODULAR FIGHTING UNIT — CAPABLE OF COVERING ANY TERRAIN AND GIVING BATTLE UNDER ALL COMBAT CONDITIONS.
OOOH! I GET SO EXCITED JUST LOOKING AT ITS MULTI-LEVEL KILL POWER!
CALM DOWN, McARTHUR. THIS IS UNSEEMLY BEHAVIOUR FOR A JUDGE... AND KINDLY REMOVE YOUR HAND FROM MY UNIFORM.

A DETACHMENT OF THOSE WAR DROIDS WILL BE GOING WITH YOU, DREDD. THEY'RE RATHER STUPID — CAN'T TALK MUCH, BUT THEY DO THEIR JOB.
H'MM... AFTER WALTER— THAT'LL BE A NICE CHANGE!
PANT PANT WE'VE ALSO SELECTED THREE OF OUR TOP JUDGES TO ASSIST YOU. JUDGE JACK, JUDGE PATTON AND JUDGE GRADGRIND. GASP
GOOD TO HAVE YOU WITH ME, GENTLEMEN. WE FOUGHT TOGETHER IN THE ROBOT REBELLION, I BELIEVE, JUDGE JACK.
THIS IS YOUR ROUTE TO MEGA CITY TWO... ACROSS A THOUSAND MILES OF THE CURSED EARTH. YOU'LL HAVE TO FACE MUTIES, SLAY-RIDERS, AND OTHER NAMELESS HORRORS CAUSED BY THE ATOMIC WARS.
IT'S CRAZY... MAN WITH HIS HYPER-TECHNOLOGY CAN TRAVEL TO THE MOON AND BEYOND — YET HE'S STILL MADE A REAL MESS OF HIS HOME PLANET.
YOU ALSO NEED A BIKE MAN FOR THE SECOND QUASAR BIKE, DREDD.
I SUGGEST—
NO! I'LL PICK MY OWN BIKER! HE'S GOT TO BE SOMEONE SPECIAL. AND I KNOW JUST THE MAN...
DREDD CLIMBED ABOARD HIS CITY-BIKE...
GET ME THE GOVERNOR OF THE MEGA-PENITENTIARY. I'M ON MY WAY TO VISIT ONE OF HIS HIGH RISK PRISONERS...
VEHICLE TESTING CENTRE
SPIKES HARVEY ROTTEN!

THE GOVERNOR APPEARED ON DREDD'S VID-COM...
SPIKES HARVEY ROTTEN? HE'S A REFORMED CHARACTER NOW, JUDGE. AT THIS MOMENT HE'S VISITING MEGA-SCHOOL THREE — TELLING THE KIDS HOW TERRIBLE IT IS TO BE A LAWBREAKER.
YOU SEE, SPIKES WANTED TO DO SOMETHING GOOD WITH HIS LIFE. WE REFORM NINETY NINE PER CENT OF OUR PRISONERS HERE, YOU KNOW.
IT'S THE OTHER ONE PER CENT I'M WORRIED ABOUT, GOVERNOR.
GOT TO GET TO MEGA-SCHOOL THREE... FAST.
AT THAT MOMENT, AT MEGA-SCHOOL THREE...
DON'T END UP LIKE ME, KIDS. I'M A LAWBREAKER! I'M DIRT! DERE AIN'T A SCRAP OF DECENCY IN ME!
SOMETIMES, WHEN I WAKE UP IN DA MORNING, KIDS... I LOOK AT MYSELF IN THE MIRROR AND I WANNA BE SICK!
WIPE DAT SMILE OFF YER FACE, KID! BEING A LAWBREAKER AIN'T NOTHIN' TO SMILE ABOUT! IT'S DUMB! D'YOU HEAR?
JUST LIKE WEARIN' DESE HANDCUFFS IS DUMB...
BOY... SPIKES IS REALLY TELLING IT FROM THE HEART... HE'S EVEN GOT ME CHOKED UP!
JUST LIKE DIS WARDER IS DUMB! HURR, HURRR!
UUUGHH CHOKE GAKKK
MEANWHILE, DREDD ARRIVES AT MEGA-SCHOOL THREE...
I ONLY HOPE I'M IN TIME...

DING DONG HELLO. YOU'RE LATE, YOU NAUGHTY BOY. PLEASE ENTER SOUND-PROOF BOX FOUR AND INSERT HANDS IN SLOT FOR ELECTRO-DISCIPLINE...THANK YOU!
DROKK IT, I'M NOT A SCHOOLBOY—I'M A JUDGE! AND WHERE DO I FIND THE CLASS WITH SPIKES HARVEY ROTTEN?
YOU'LL FIND HIM IN HISTORY-FIVE.
...THANK YOU.
MY, MY. YOU JUDGES ARE RUDE, AREN'T YOU. NOT ENOUGH DISCIPLINE, THAT'S THE TROUBLE...THANK YOU.
JUDGE DREDD!
DROP DER GUN, JUDGEY—OR DA KID GETS A DRAFT BETWEEN HIS EARS!
BY STOMM! I GOT NO CHOICE!
JUST ONE CHANCE...
DAT'S BETTER, JUDGEY. NOW BACK OFF—NICE AND EASY... DIS KID IS MY PASSPORT TO FREEDOM!
DREDD PRESSED THE 'ANCIENT HISTORY' BUTTON ON THE HOLOGRAM CONSOLE...
AND SUDDENLY...
WHAT...?
DOWN, KIDS!

GOTTA TAKE SPIKES ALIVE
AAAHH!
YOU'RE NOT TAKIN' ME THIS TIME, DREDD!
THAT'S WHERE YOU'RE WRONG, SPIKES!
I'M TAKING YOU...ALL THE WAY ACROSS THE CURSED EARTH...TO MEGA-CITY TWO ON A SUICIDE MISSION...
...HOW DO YOU LIKE THAT, SPIKES?
NOOOO!
YOU WANT TO DO SOMETHING GOOD WITH YOUR LIFE...YOU GOT THE CHANCE NOW...'COS YOU'RE THE BEST BIKER IN THE BUSINESS...
...AND YOU KNOW THE CURSED EARTH WELL FROM YOUR DAYS OF GUN RUNNING TO THE MUTIES!
RIGHT, SPIKE?
T-THAT WAS NEVER PROVED...
MAYBE I'M A BIT DEAF, SPIKES— BUT I CAN'T HEAR YOU VOLUNTEERING FOR THIS MISSION OF MERCY THAT'S GOING TO SAVE THOUSANDS FROM THE PLAGUE!
I VOLUNTEER! I VOLUNTEER!
COULD YOU SPEAK A LITTLE LOUDER?
I'M PROUD OF YOU, SPIKES! PROUD!
AAAAH!

That's it for our first Cursed Earth extract. Pick up the story in Rebellion's *The Complete Case Files 02*.

PROG 168
7 JUNE 80
AND
TORNADO
Malaysia $1.00
New Zealand 35c
Australia 35c
South Africa 35c
Mercury 17g
Venus 10g
Mars 15g
Asteroid Belt 20g
Saturn 84g
Neptune 87g
Pluto 93g
12p
EARTH MONEY
IN ORBIT EVERY MONDAY
BRITAIN'S Nº1 COMIC HERO LAYS DOWN THE LAW
ANY QUESTIONS?
DREDD
McMahon

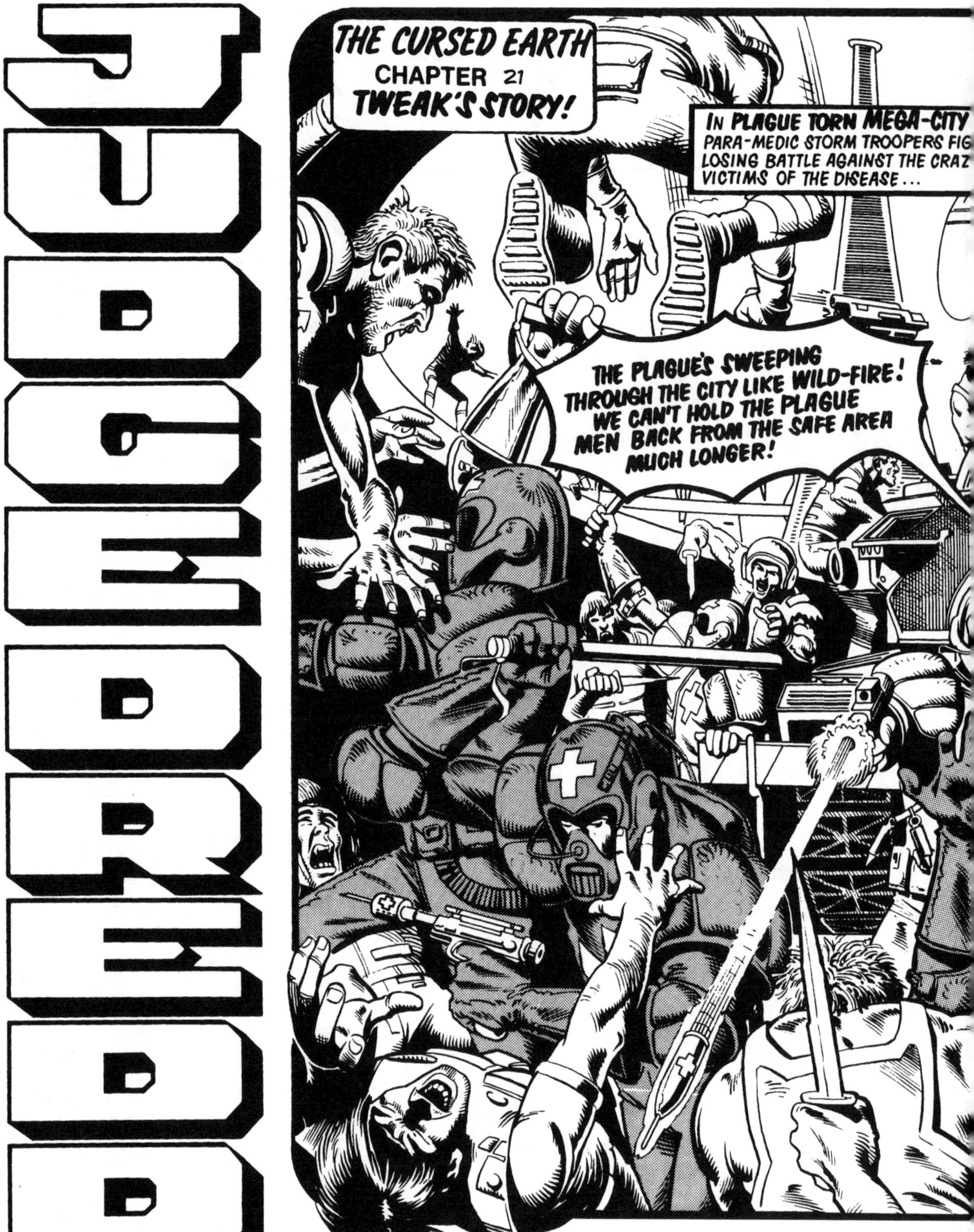

THE CURSED EARTH
CHAPTER 21
TWEAK'S STORY!

IN PLAGUE TORN MEGA-CITY
PARA-MEDIC STORM TROOPERS FIG
LOSING BATTLE AGAINST THE CRAZ
VICTIMS OF THE DISEASE...

THE PLAGUE'S SWEEPING THROUGH THE CITY LIKE WILD-FIRE! WE CAN'T HOLD THE PLAGUE MEN BACK FROM THE SAFE AREA MUCH LONGER!

ONLY SOMEONE CAN
THROUGH FROM MEGA-
ONE WITH THE VACCINE,
SARGE!
LL THEN WE KEEP
ING THE TRANQUILISERS!
LIFT
9
ERV
MEDIC RIOT COMMANDO
FIRST CLASS
SERGEANT OF THE PARA-
ICS SNARLED THROUGH
MOUTH-PIECE OF HIS
IRATOR...
WHAT DO THEM YANKEES IN
MEGA-CITY ONE CARE? THEY'LL
JUST LEAVE US TO DIE!
RECKON THEY'LL BE GLAD
MEGA-CITY TWO IS FINISHED!
THERE'LL BE NO HELP FROM
THEM!

BUT AT THAT MOMENT, JUDGE DREDD'S AMAZING JOURNEY ACROSS THE CURSED EARTH--WITH THE VITAL VACCINE--WAS ALMOST OVER. HIS LAND-RAIDER WAS APPROACHING DEATH-VALLEY...
MEGA-CITY TWO
THE CURSED EARTH
MEGA-CITY ONE
THEN...
THE VACCINE REFRIGERATION UNIT'S PACKED UP. GOING TO TAKE A COUPLE OF HOURS TO TRACE THE FAULT, JUDGE DREDD.
I'LL GIVE YOU THIRTY MINUTES.
WE'RE ON THE LAST LAP NOW, JUDGEY. THE WORST OF THE CURSED EARTH IS BEHIND US... HEY! OL' FREAK FACE TWEAK IS STARTING TO GET THE HANG OF OUR LINGO!
HELLLLO, SPIIIIKES, HOW ARRRRE YOU? VERRRRY WELLLL, THANNNNK YOU.
1+1=2
YOU'LL NEVER BE AS SMART AS US HUMANS, FREAK FACE--BUT MAYBE I CAN LEARN YER A BIT. WATCH CAREFULLY... ONE PLUS ONE EQUALS TWO. GEDDIT?
THAT'S GOOD, SPIIIIKES, VERRRRY GOOD. KEEP UP THE GOOD WORKKKK!
NO, NOT ME, YOU STUPID ALIEN! I'M TRYING TO TEACH YOU! NOW YOU HAVE A GO!
TO SPIKE'S AMAZEMENT...
TWURRP!
I-I DON'T BELIEVE IT!

HE MUST BE A FLAMIN' GENIUS!
YOU'VE BEEN HOLDING OUT ON US, TWEAK. I FIGURE YOU OWE US AN EXPLANATION.
I HADDD NO CHOICE, JUDGE DREDDDDD...
...ITTT WAS THE ONLY WAYYYY TO SAVE MYYYYY PEOPLE...
TWEAK TOLD DREDD AND SPIKES ABOUT HIS PLANET... THE VAST CITIES DEEP BENEATH THE GROUND -- CLOSE TO THE ROCK FARMS WHERE HIS PEOPLE HARVESTED THEIR FOOD ... GOLD, DIAMONDS AND OTHER ROCKS...
TWALK?
TWURK!
...AND TWEAK'S JOB. THE NEAREST HUMAN WORD TO IT WAS 'PRESIDENT' OR 'LEADER'.
THEN ONE DAY, THE ALIENS DETECTED A STRANGE SPACE-SHIP APPROACHING THEIR PLANET... THE FIRST STAR-SHIP FROM EARTH...!
TWEAK ORDERED THE PLANET'S SURFACE TO BE EVACUATED AND CITY ENTRANCES CAMOUFLAGED ...UNTIL MORE WAS KNOWN ABOUT THE STRANGERS.
A POD FROM THE STARSHIP LANDED...
KEEP YOUR EYES OPEN FOR ANY ALIEN SPECIMENS WE CAN TAKE BACK, MEN. BUT REMEMBER-- WE'VE STRICT INSTRUCTIONS TO LEAVE INTELLIGENT ALIENS ALONE.
YES. WE COME IN PEACE FOR ALL MAN-KIND.

BUT THE ALIENS' MIND MACHINES PROBED THE HUMANS' BRAINS... AND PROJECTED THE HUMANS' MEMORIES... OF GREED AND HATRED...
...AND BRUTAL WARS!
SOME MEMBERS OF TWEAK'S COUNCIL ARGUED THAT THIS WAS IN THE HUMANS' PAST... THE ASTRONAUTS GENUINELY CAME IN PEACE AND SHOULD BE WELCOMED.
TWEAK CRUNCHED A SAPPHIRE AND THOUGHT ABOUT IT...
THEN, USING HIS POWERS OF PRE-COGNITION, TWEAK PROJECTED A PICTURE OF HOW HUMANS MIGHT BEHAVE ON THEIR PLANET IN FUTURE.
IT WAS NOT PRETTY!
HUMANS COULD NEVER CONTROL THEIR GREED FOR DIAMONDS AND OTHER RICHES, THEY WOULD BE BACK -- WANTING MINING RIGHTS, BRINGING POLLUTION AND DISEASE.

OF COURSE TWEAK MIGHT BE WRONG. THE HUMANS MIGHT HAVE BEEN REALLY WONDERFUL. BUT THE ALIENS DECIDED NOT TO TAKE THE CHANCE. THERE WOULD BE NO CONTACT.
KLIK!
BUT, AT THAT MOMENT...
LOOK-- THERE'S A COUPLE OF SPECIMENS!
THE YOUNG ALIENS HAD DISOBEYED THE ORDER TO REMAIN UNDERGROUND. CURIOUS, THEY EXAMINED THE HUMANS' "FUR"...
I'VE NEVER SEEN DAFTER LOOKING ANIMALS THAN THESE TWO... PUT THEM IN A SPECIMEN CAGE FOR FURTHER EXAMINATION.
TWUURP!
MEANWHILE, THEIR GOLDEN FURRED MOTHER WAS OUT ANXIOUSLY LOOKING FOR THEM...
TWAAL!
TWEAK HAD WATCHED, HORRIFIED, AS SHE TOO WAS CAUGHT AND CAGED...
IT WAS HIS MATE AND CHILDREN!
TWEAK HAD TWO CHOICES...
1. HE COULD RESCUE HIS FAMILY BY SHOWING THE HUMANS HOW ADVANCED HIS RACE WERE--BUT THEN THE HUMANS WOULD NEVER LEAVE THEM ALONE.
2. HE COULD SACRIFICE HIMSELF AND HIS FAMILY --PRETEND TO BE DUMB ANIMALS AND GO BACK WITH THE HUMANS TO THEIR TERRIBLE PLANET EARTH...

HE HAD NO CHOICE. AS LEADER, THE FUTURE OF HIS PEOPLE AND PLANET CAME FIRST... HE SAID HIS SAD FAREWELLS...
TWEAK!
TWEAK!
THEN...
LOOK-- HERE COMES ANOTHER ONE-- WALKING STRAIGHT INTO A CAGE.
BOY! I SAID THOSE ANIMALS WAS REALLY THICK!
CLANG!
TWOLK!
TWEXX?
LET'S GO, MEN. THIS PLANET AIN'T WORTH RETURNIN' TO IN A HURRY!
TWEAK STOPPED FOR A MOMENT...
WOULD YOU LIKE TO TRYYYY A LITTLE SANDSTONE, JUDGE DREDDDD? IT'S VERRRRY TASTY?
NO THANKS, TWEAK!
CARRY ON WITH YER STORY, TWEAK OLD BUDDY. WE'LL GET BACK TO THAT BIT ABOUT THE DIAMONDS LATER! WHAT YOU NEED IS A -ER- BUSINESS MANAGER LIKE ME TO PROTECT YOUR INTERESTS.
BUT DREDD WAS PUZZLED...
THE ALIEN TRICKED US HUMANS TO SAVE HIS PLANET. SO WHY IS HE TELLING ME AND SPIKES HIS SECRET NOW? UNLESS IT DOESN'T MATTER... UNLESS WE'LL NEVER GET THE CHANCE TO TELL ANYONE ELSE!
NEXT PROG: ALIEN MESSIAH!

GET SPACED OUT WITH JUDGE DREDD INSIDE!

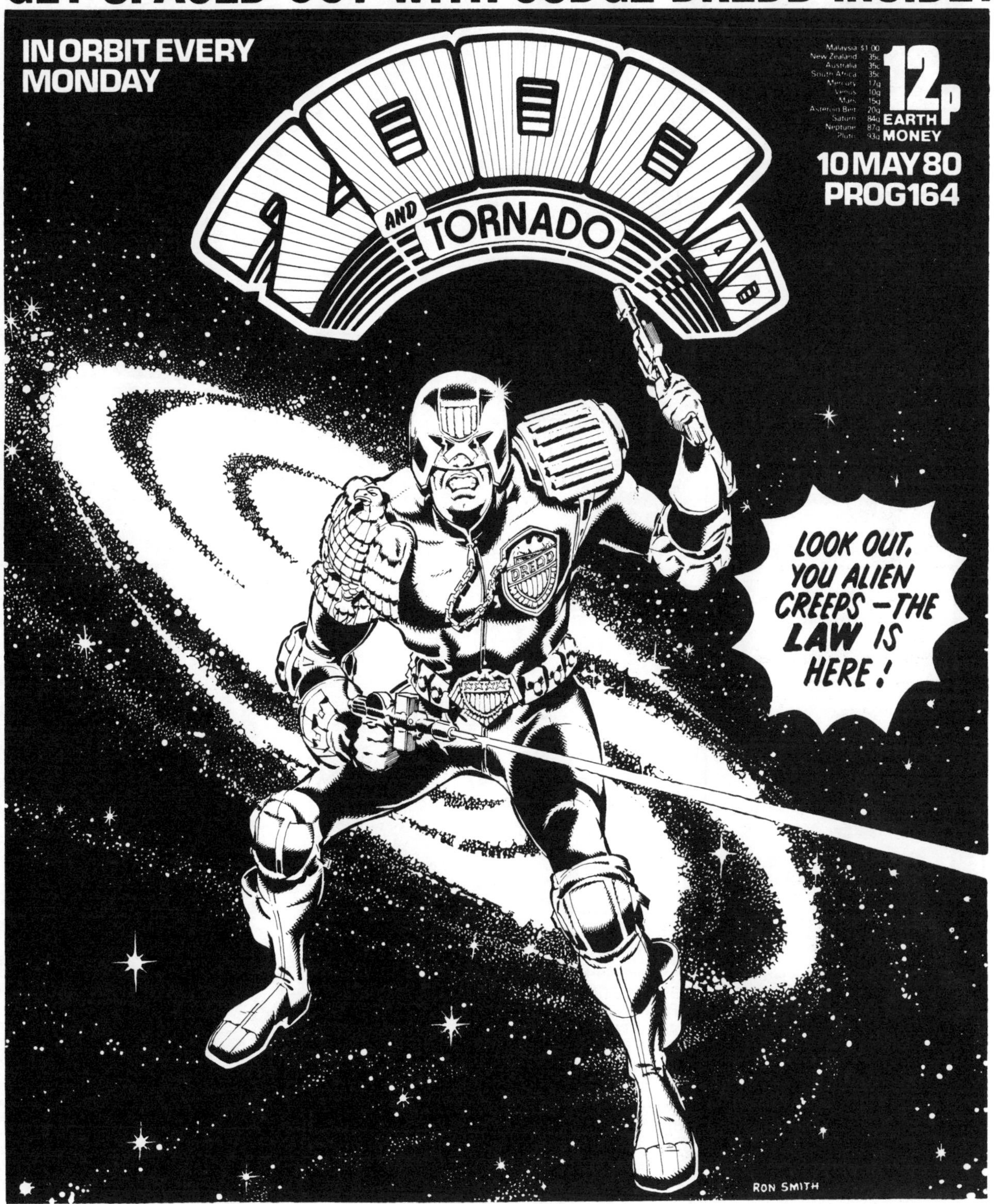

IN ORBIT EVERY MONDAY
Malaysia $1.00
New Zealand 35c
Australia 35c
South Africa 35c
Mercury 17g
Venus 10g
Mars 15g
Asteroid Belt 20g
Saturn 84g
Neptune 87g
Pluto 93g
12p EARTH MONEY
10 MAY 80
PROG164
AND TORNADO
LOOK OUT, YOU ALIEN CREEPS — THE LAW IS HERE!
RON SMITH

THE CURSED EARTH
CHAPTER 22

TWEAK'S STORY

JUDGE DREDD

WHILE JUDGE DREDD'S 'LAND RAIDER' WAS BEING REPAIRED, THE ALIEN TWE
CONTINUED HIS STRANGE STORY... HOW HE AND HIS FAMILY HAD BEEN KIDNAPPE
FROM THEIR HOME PLANET AND BROUGHT AS SPECIMENS TO EARTH...

TWEAK!
TWEAK!
TWEAK!

EISINGER

...BUT HE LOOKS AND ACTS SO DUMB!

INCREDIBLE! OUR TESTS SHOW THAT THIS CREATURE HAS A GREATER INTELLIGENCE THAN US!

2000 A.D.
Credit Card:
SCRIPT ROBOT PAT MILLS
ART ROBOT BRIAN BOLLAND
LETTERING ROBOT PETE KNIGHT
COMPU-73E

H'MM... MAYBE HE IS ACTING...
WE'LL RUN THE TESTS AGAIN. IF HE IS HE WON'T BE ABLE TO KEEP IT UP FOR LONG!
DR. CH
62
BUT TWEAK SUFFERED ALL THE HORRIBLE TESTS WITHOUT REVEALING HE WAS INTELLIGENT...
FOR ONLY BY HIS SACRIFICE COULD HE SAVE HIS PEOPLE AND HIS PLANET... SAVE THEM A FATE WORSE THAN DEATH...
...HUMAN BEINGS!

TAKE HIM DOWN.
IF THE HUMANS KNEW THE TRUTH— THEY WOULD RETURN TO HIS PLANET. DISCOVER THE UNDERGROUND FARMS WHERE HIS PEOPLE HARVESTED GOLD, DIAMONDS AND OTHER ROCKS FOR FOOD—
THE HUMANS WOULD MINE IT AND HIS PEOPLE STARVE... WHILE THE HUMANS GREW RICH AS THEY SPREAD THEIR POLLUTION AND DISEASES...
GIVE HIM THE ALIEN I.Q. TESTS AGAIN.
NOW, TWEAK— THIS IS A BOOK. WHAT DO YOU DO WITH A BOOK?
ENCYCLOPEDIA OF EARTH
TWAAAAWK?
NO, YOU DON'T EAT IT, YOU DUMB ANIMAL!
TWOKK!
TWOL!
THE THICK BRUTE DOESN'T UNDERSTAND WEAPONS EITHER— HE'S POINTING THE GUN WE GAVE HIM AT HIMSELF!
HE CAN'T EVEN WALK THROUGH A DOOR! YES, I'M AFRAID HE'S DEFINITELY STUPID!

AND VICIOUS WITH IT! ALL DOCTOR ARMSTRONG DID WAS TO OFFER TWEAK'S KIDDIES SOME SWEETIES. GET THEM ALL OUT OF MY SIGHT— THEY'RE OF NO MORE INTEREST.
HSSSSS!

TWEAK'S FEARS ABOUT THE DARK SIDE OF HUMAN NATURE WERE REALISED WHEN LATER HE AND HIS FAMILY WERE SOLD INTO SLAVERY...
HE'S A STRONG LOOKING ANIMAL. I'LL BUY HIM FOR MA FERRY.
I'LL TAKE THE OTHERS.

MISS SOPHIE WILL LIKE TO PLAY WITH THE LITTLE FURRY ONES UP AT THE BIG HOUSE.
OH, YETH!
BUT SOON— UP AT THE BIG HOUSE...
DON'T WANT THEM NO MORE! THEY BIT ME WHEN I TRIED TO PUT A DRETH ON THEM!
HSSSSS!
I'M GOING TO THCWEAM AND THCWEAM AND THCWEAM!
NOW DON'T WORRY YER PRETTY LI'L' HEAD 'BOUT THEM VICIOUS CRITTURS, MISS SOPHIE. I'LL TAKE 'EM OUTSIDE AND-ER-DEAL WITH THEM.

IN THE PLANTATION, TWEAK'S GOLDEN FURRED MATE HAD BEEN WORKING. SUDDENLY— WITH HER ALIEN POWERS OF FORESEEING THE FUTURE— SHE KNEW WHAT WAS GOING TO HAPPEN—
TWAAAAR!

DESPERATELY RAN TO THEIR AID—
SO YOU WANT SOME TOO, HUH?

TRIED TO TAKE THE BULLETS FOR THEM—
TWEAK! TWEAK! TWEAK!

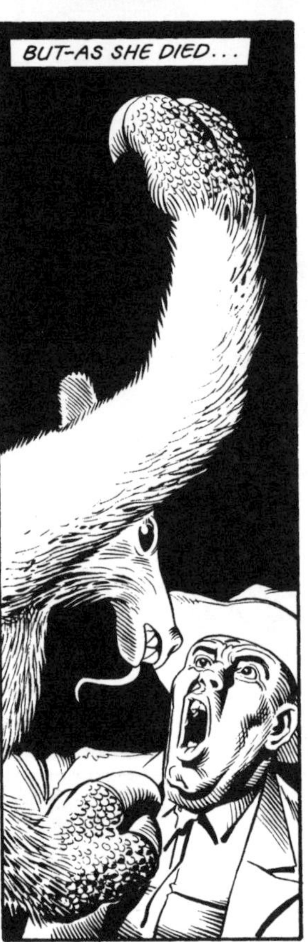
BUT-AS SHE DIED...

AAAGGGH!

MEANWHILE, TWEAK— DESPERATE TO BE REUNITED WITH HIS FAMILY— HAD ESCAPED... ONLY TO FIND THEM— TOO LATE...
TWAAAAAAW!

AAAAAAK
THEN—AS JUDGE DREDD ALREADY KNEW—TWEAK HAD BURIED THEM ACCORDING TO THE CUSTOM ON HIS PLANET... LAYING ROCKS ON THEIR GRAVE—"FOOD" FOR THEIR JOURNEY AFTER DEATH...
THAT'S A HECK OF A STORY, TWEAK OLD BUDDY. BUT THE LAND-RAIDER'S BEEN REPAIRED. JUST DEATH VALLEY TO CROSS AND WE'VE MADE IT.
WE'LL BE WITH YOU IN A MINUTE, SPIKES.
YOU SACRIFICED YOURSELF AND YOUR FAMILY— TO SAVE YOUR PLANET. BUT WHAT MAKES YOU THINK I WON'T REPORT THE UNDERGROUND MINERAL FARMS ON YOUR PLANET—AND A FLEET OF MINING SHIPS BE SENT OUT TO TEAR YOUR HOME APART?
I TRRRRUST YOU, JUDGE DREDDDDD.
AND SPIKES?
OH, NO. POOR SPIIIIIIKES. BUT ITTTT DIDN'T REALLY MATTTTER IF HE HEARD. HE WILL DIIIIE IN DEATH VALLLLLLEY. IT IS VERY SADDDDD.

That's it for the Cursed Earth in this book! Pick up the story in Rebellion's *The Complete Case Files 02*.

FOLLOWING THE DEATH OF THE TYRANT CAL, **MEGA-CITY ONE** SLOWLY BEGAN TO RETURN TO NORMAL. BUT THERE WERE SOME PLACES IN THE CITY WHERE LAW AND ORDER HAD BROKEN DOWN **TOO FAR**... PLACES WHERE **EVEN JUDGES WERE NOT SAFE TO VENTURE!**

JUDGE DREDD

JIM NAUSEA PLEADED THE CASE FOR THE "DEFENCE"...

MY CLIENT WOULD JUST LIKE TA SAY THAT HE'S AS GUILTY AS SIN! SO HE WANTS TA PAY THE MAXIMUM PENALTY!
THERES NO JUSTUS
THERES JUST US

I FIND THE DEFENDANT GUILTY AS CHARGED — AN' SENTENCE HIM TA GIVE EVERYTHING HE OWNS TA ME!
THERES NO JUSTUS
THERES JUST US
STRIP THE CRUMBO AN' GET RID OF HIM!

DARN IT! WHY CAN'T YOU FIND A REAL JUDGE WHEN YOU WANT ONE?
THE COSMIC PUNKS ARE THE LAW IN THIS SECTOR. ANY JUDGE WHO COMES IN HERE — HE DON'T COME OUT!
PAY TOLL HERE
COSMIC PUNKS TERRITORY

IN THE REAL HALL OF JUSTICE, THE SITUATION WAS WORRYING NEW CHIEF JUDGE GRIFFIN —

THE WAR AGAINST CAL ALLOWED THE STREET GANGS TO COME BACK IN FORCE. IT'S WORST HERE, IN SOUTHSIDE SECTOR 41. THE COSMIC PUNKS HAVE SET THEMSELVES UP AS JUDGES AND DECLARED A NO-GO AREA.
STAMP ON IT SHARP! ORGANISE AN ASSAULT SQUAD — FIFTY MEN SHOULD DO!
I DISAGREE! WE'RE GIVING THESE CHEAP LAWBREAKERS MORE CREDIT THAN THEY DESERVE.

THE STREET GANGS HAVE LOST THEIR FEAR OF US. IT'S TIME WE GAVE IT BACK TO THEM...
LET'S SHOW THEM ONE JUDGE IS WORTH A HUNDRED PUNKS — COSMIC OR OTHERWISE!

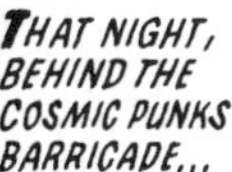
THAT NIGHT, BEHIND THE COSMIC PUNKS' BARRICADE...

WORD IS THE JUDGES MIGHT HIT US TONIGHT. GESTAPO BOB SAYS TA KEEP YER BLASTER-FINGERS OILED.
NATCH, FILE-TOOTH.
HEY, I HEAR AN ENGINE...

IT'S ONLY A GARBAGE TRUCK.
SO, WHO'S THAT CRUMBO IN THE CAB ?

IT'S JUDGE DREDD! BUT—WHERE'S THE OTHERS ?
CITY GARBAGE.
THERE ARE NO OTHERS. ONE JUDGE IS ENOUGH FOR PUNKS LIKE YOU !
YOU'RE UNDER ARREST !

GET HIM — AAGHH!
I WASN'T TALKING FOR THE GOOD OF MY HEALTH, PAL !

AAAH!

HOW WOULD YOU LIKE A THIRD EYE TO GO WITH THOSE FILED TEETH ? THEY SAY IT HELPS YOU TO SEE THE FUTURE !
I-I AIN'T GONNA HAVE NO FUTURE WITH A THIRD EYE ! I SURRENDER !

DREDD HANDCUFFED THE CAPTIVES AMONG THE GARBAGE —
LAWBREAKERS NEED A DEMONSTRATION OF OUR POWER — AND PERHAPS SO DO THE JUDGES THEMSELVES. MORALE HAS BEEN LOW SINCE CAL — OTHERWISE TRASH LIKE THESE PUNKS WOULD NEVER GET OUT OF HAND!
FOLLOW ME AT TEN PACES, TRUCK.
AFFIRMATIVE, SIR.

DO YOU HEAR ME, PUNKS? THIS IS JUDGE DREDD AND I'VE COME TO COLLECT THE GARBAGE!
HE'S COME ALONE! HE'S GOTTA BE CRAZY —

TWO ON THE ROOF — STEEL-TIPPED HIGH-PENETRATION!
AAAAAH!

MAN FIRING FROM CORNER WINDOW —
UGGH

HOTSHOT!

DREDD'S LAWGIVER FIRED SIX KINDS OF BULLET. THE HOTSHOT HAD A HEAT-SEEKING HOMING HEAD!
AIIEEE!

ONLY DREDD'S SUPERB TRAINING AND YEARS OF EXPERIENCE SAVED HIM THAT NIGHT IN THE STRONGHOLD OF THE COSMIC PUNKS. BUT AS THE GARBAGE TRUCK FILLED, RESISTANCE DWINDLED AWAY –
I'VE COME FOR YOU, GESTAPO BOB! I WANT YOU WITH THE REST OF THE GARBAGE!
HE'S TOO GOOD FOR US, GESTAPO. YOU SAW HOW NOBODY COULD TOUCH HIM! WE GOTTA GIVE IN!
NOBODY QUITS – NOT AS LONG AS I'M CHIEF JUDGE OF THE COSMIC PUNKS!
THERES NO JUSTUS
THERES JUST US
GARBAGE
I DIDN'T THINK I'D WAIT FOR A REPLY. IT WAS KIND OF PREDICTABLE!
DON'T GET UP, GESTAPO BOB! I WANT A LITTLE *TALK* WITH YOU!
OOF!
I HEAR YOU'VE BEEN CALLING YOURSELF ***CHIEF JUDGE***, BOB. I DON'T LIKE THAT, BOB. IT MAKES ME KIND OF ANGRY – ESPECIALLY COMING FROM A CHEAP PUNK LIKE YOU, BOB. WHAT ARE YOU, BOB?
I... I'M A CH-CHEAP PUNK...
I'M SORRY, BOB – I'M GETTING A LITTLE DEAF. COULD WE HAVE THAT AGAIN – A LITTLE ***LOUDER*** THIS TIME?

I'M A CHEAP PUNK!

OUTSIDE...
DREDD
DREDD TO CONTROL. I WANT A TEAM OF AMBULANCES TO ATTEND WOUNDED IN SOUTHSIDE SECTOR 41. NO BACK-UP UNIT NEEDED – IT'S ALL QUIET HERE... REPEAT – ALL QUIET.

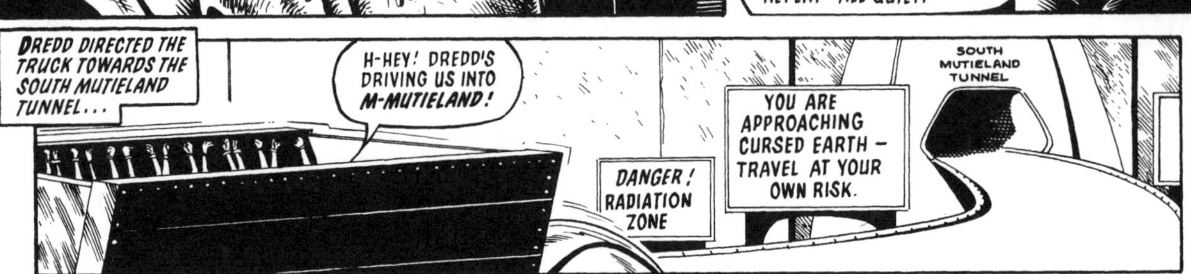
DREDD DIRECTED THE TRUCK TOWARDS THE SOUTH MUTIELAND TUNNEL...
H-HEY! DREDD'S DRIVING US INTO M-MUTIELAND!
DANGER! RADIATION ZONE
YOU ARE APPROACHING CURSED EARTH – TRAVEL AT YOUR OWN RISK.
SOUTH MUTIELAND TUNNEL

ON THE OTHER SIDE OF THE TUNNEL –
MEGA-CITY 1 NO ENTRY
AS PUNISHMENT FOR YOUR CRIMES I REMOVE YOUR CITIZENSHIP. YOU WILL NOT BE ALLOWED TO ENTER MEGA-CITY ONE FOR TEN YEARS!
Y-YOU CAN'T DO THIS! THIS PLACE IS A HELL ON EARTH!
GIVE ME TWENTY YEARS – THIRTY – ONLY PLEASE DON'T BANISH ME!

PLEASE! DON'T GO!
HARSH BUT NECESSARY. LET THEM SERVE AS AN EXAMPLE. LET EVERY MAN KNOW THAT CITIZENSHIP IS A PRIVILEGE – NOT A RIGHT!
IN THE NAME OF MERCY, DON'T DO THIS TO US!

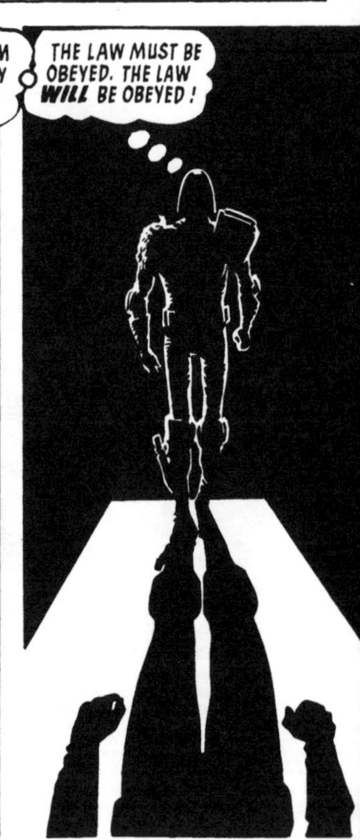
THE LAW MUST BE OBEYED. THE LAW WILL BE OBEYED!

JUDGE DREDD

KENNEDY SPACE-PORT, MEGA-CITY ONE! JUMPING OFF POINT FOR THE PLANETS!
WILL THOSE PASSENGERS WITH ANYTHING TO DECLARE PLEASE GO TO CUSTOMS GATE "Y"
SPACE AXIS ZERO ONE
HAVE YOU ZONED YET?
"ANYTHING TO DECLARE". HUH? HOW ABOUT A HEART FULL OF HATE FOR A MAN. HATE THAT'S KEPT ME ALIVE THROUGH TWENTY LONG YEARS OF HELL!
BUT ONE MAN KEEPS TO HIMSELF, A LONER IN THE SHADOWS...
YEAH... THINGS HAVE SURE CHANGED AROUND HERE. IT WAS JUST ONE SHUTTLE A WEEK GOING OUT OF KENNEDY WHEN I LEFT FOR TITAN, A LIFETIME AGO...
...MY LIFETIME! BEFORE THEY DID THOSE THINGS TO ME... HURT ME INSIDE...
2000 A.D.
THRILL 2
THE RETURN OF RICO!

CAN I HELP YOU, SIR.?
LEAVE ME ALONE! GET YOUR HANDS OFF ME! DO YOU HEAR?

THE MAN MADE HIS WAY TO A VIEW PHONE, AND...
GOOD MORNING! MEGA-CITY JUSTICE H.Q.! PLEASE STATE YOUR BUSINESS.
TRI-DEE
MY BUSINESS IS PERSONAL! I WANT TO SPEAK TO A JUDGE... JUDGE DREDD!

I'M SORRY, SIR. THE JUDGE IS OUT ON PATROL.
JUST TELL HIM I CALLED... MY NAME IS DREDD... JUDGE DREDD!

BUT, SIR, THAT'S IMPOSSIBLE... THERE'S ONLY ONE JUDGE DREDD!
THAT'S RIGHT, SWEETHEART
AFTER TONIGHT ... THERE'S ONLY GONNA BE... ME!

MEANWHILE...
AAAH!
OKAY, YOU LAWBREAKERS! COME ON OUT SLOWLY - OR DO YOU WANT SOME MORE?
URGENT CALL FOR YOU FROM H.Q., JUDGE!

WE CAN HANDLE THEM NOW, JUDGE!
SORRY TO INTERRUPT YOU, JUDGE. BUT THIS HORRIBLE MAN PHONED. I KNOW IT'S CRAZY - BUT HE SAID HIS NAME WAS... JUDGE DREDD!
SO YOU CAME BACK, RICO. LIKE I ALWAYS KNEW YOU WOULD...
BEFORE THE NIGHT IS OUT, ONE OF US WILL HAVE TO DIE!

AND, AT THE JUDGE'S APARTMENT, MARIA - DREDD'S ITALIAN HOUSEKEEPER - OPENS THE DOOR TO... HORROR!
I AM-A BUSY COOKING THE-A PAELLA. WHATEVER YOU SELLING, THE JUDGE NO WANT IT...
EEEEK! YOUR FACE!
HE'LL BUY THIS! LADY! LET ME IN!
THAT'S HER OUT OF THE WAY. NOW I'M GONNA MAKE A FEW ADJUSTMENT'S TO THE ROOM'S VENTILATION ... AND WAIT FOR DREDD...
LATER, THE JUDGE RETURNS, MOVING SILENTLY UP THE STAIRS...
I KNOW YOU'RE UP THERE, RICO. IN A STAKE-OUT, THERE WAS NO ONE TO BEAT YOU...
THE DOOR... OR THE FIRE ESCAPE... WHICH HAVE YOU GOT COVERED?
DREDD KICKED OPEN THE DOOR...
FREEZE, RICO... UUUH?
TRIPLE BLUFF, JOE! NOW DROP THE GUN...
DREDD
UHHH... FREEZING IN HERE... AND
CHOKE NO AIR... MY RESPIRATOR...
THAT'S RIGHT, JOE BLACK. AIRLESS COLD LIKE TITAN - I WANT YOU TO KNOW HOW IT FELT...
ONLY IT DON'T AFFECT ME...
I CAN EAT VACUUM AND LIVE!
YOUR RESPIRATOR GIVES YOU JUST TWENTY MINUTES OXYGEN, JOE. TWENTY MINUTES TO PAY FOR TWENTY YEARS...
LET'S TALK ABOUT IT. TALK ABOUT OLD TIMES...
WHILE YOUR BLOOD TURNS TO ICE AND I WATCH YOU DIE!
UUUH... OKAY, RICO... LET'S ... TALK...

JUDGES ARE RAISED FROM THE CRADLE... THAT'S HOW IT WAS WITH US, EH, JOE? WE WERE **CLONES**. TWO IDENTICAL PEOPLE... NOT TWINS... BUT **DUPLICATES**! THAT'S HOW IT ALL BEGAN"...

AT GENETIC CONTROL...
"This excellent dna structure. These two are perfect material for Judges"!

"I TAUGHT YOU EVERYTHING I KNEW... UNTIL PASSING OUT DAY WHEN WE BECAME ROOKIE JUDGES. I CAME FIRST... YOU CAME SECOND".

WE WERE THE BEST OF FRIENDS THROUGH JUDGE ACADEMY. AFTER ALL WE WERE THE SAME PERSON. ONLY I WAS BETTER THAN YOU... SO I HELPED YOU ALL I COULD, JOE"..

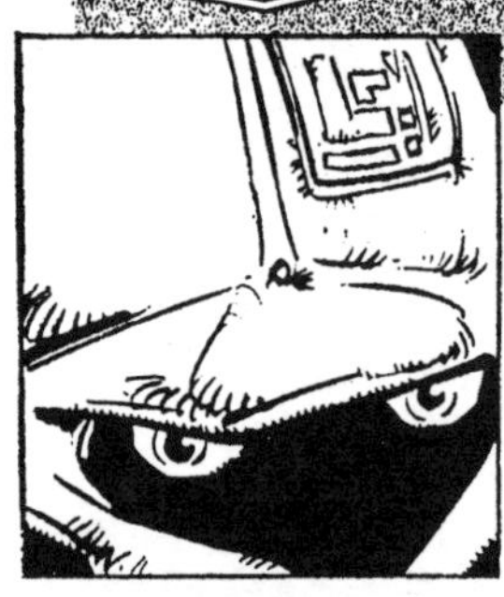

"Excellent marksmanship, Rico Dredd. Joe Dredd, you're not fast enough on the draw and your aim is way off target"!

Congratulations, You two!
"If it hadn't been for you, Rico, I'd never have made it"!

YEAH, RICO. BUT YOU WERE **TOO** SMART. YOU HAD TO FOUL THINGS UP... BY TAKINGS **BRIBES** AND RUNNING A **PROTECTION RACKET**"..

"THAT'S WHEN I HAD TO MAKE A **TERRIBLE DECISION**, RICO"...

"YOU SHOULDN'T HAVE DONE THAT, JOE. THE PUNISHMENT FOR JUDGES IS STERN. **TWENTY YEARS ON THE PENAL COLONY ON TITAN**! YOU DON'T GET MANY BUSTED JUDGES... SO THE GUARDS GIVE YOU **INDIVIDUAL TREATMENT**"!

Joe! Listen, we can make this look like an **accident**!
No way, Rico, I'm takin' you in!

Please, Rico... Can't pay you anymore...
You'll pay with your life, then!

I hate bent Judges, Rico, so I'm gonna bend you till you break!

"THEY SEAL UP YOUR MOUTH AND NOSE, ADAPT YOUR BODY TO WORK IN VACUUM WITHOUT A CLUMSY SPACE SUIT"...
"AND EVERY DAY I LOOKED AT THE LITTLE PIN PRICK OF LIGHT IN THE SKY THAT WAS PLANET EARTH...AND I SWORE I'D GET EVEN WITH YOU, JOE."
Can't...Take... Much...More!
Keep at it, Rico!
I'll be back! I'll survive!
2070
SWORE I'D GET REVENGE FOR WHAT YOU DID TO ME! LOOK AT ME, JOE OLD BUDDY!
LOOK AT ME!
RICO...STOP... WHILE THERE'S TIME.
NO, RICO...DON'T MAKE ME KILL YOU...
BECAUSE YOU KNOW I'M FASTER, HUH? YOU'RE YELLOW, JOE! DRAW, DARN YOU!
NO, BUT I'LL DO YOU ONE LAST FAVOUR. I'LL SHOOT YOU QUICK. YOUR GUN'S BACK IN YOUR BOOT HOLSTER. DRAW!
DRAW, I SAID!
AAAAH!
OKAY, RICO... IF THAT'S THE WAY YOU WANT IT!

...YOU...YOU...
CAN'T BE FASTER THAN R-RICO..!
TWENTY YEARS ON TITAN... SLOWED YOU DOWN A SPLIT SECOND... BUT YOU WERE THE BEST, RICO... THE BEST...

DREDD CALLED JUSTICE CENTRAL AND AS AIR AND WARMTH POURED BACK INTO THE ROOM...
I SEE YOU GOT HIM... HE'S JUST DIED...
NO. RICO DIED A LONG TIME AGO...

WE'LL TAKE THE BODY NOW, DREDD!
NO!...I...OWE... RICO... I'LL DO IT...ALONE...
BUT-BUT YOU'RE IN NO FIT STATE, DREDD... YOU'LL NEVER MAKE IT!

I'LL MAKE IT...! HE-HE AIN'T HEAVY- HE'S MY BROTHER!

STRANGE...RICO AND JOE THEY WERE THE SAME PERSON YET ONE GREW UP TO UPHOLD THE LAW THE OTHER TO DESPISE IT. GOOD AND EVIL...
THAT'S SOMETHING THE SCIENTISTS STILL CAN'T CONTROL. THEY CAN'T CONTROL MEN LIKE... JUDGE DREDD!

JUDGE
JUDGE DREDD
VIENNA
4 AM IN DREDD'S ROOMS. THE VID-SCREEN LIGHTS UP —
I'VE GOT YOUR DEAR LITTLE NIECE, DREDD! SHE'S GOING TO DIE — AND NOTHING YOU CAN DO WILL SAVE HER!
VIENNA!
HE-HE'S HURTING ME, UNCLE JOE! HELP ME! HELP ME!
THE VID-SCREEN COMPUTER TRACED THE CALL —
THE CALL CAME FROM THIS ADDRESS. THE CALLER'S NAME WAS —
-19230 SIGMA STREET DISTRICT 892.
HARRY CARMEN — I KNOW HIM. I PUT HIM DOWN FOR SIX YEARS FOR A COMPUTER SWINDLE. HE'S AN ELECTRONICS GENIUS.
NOW HARRY C IS TRYING TO GET AT ME THROUGH MY NIECE... RICO'S KID...
POOR VIENNA. HASN'T SHE SUFFERED ENOUGH BECAUSE OF ME...?

DREDD'S MIND FLASHED BACK...
SWING ME AGAIN, UNCLE JOE!
YOUNG MISS VIENNA ADORES YOU, SIR. SHE NEVER STOPS TALKING ABOUT YOU. YOU SHOULD SEE MORE OF HER.
IT'S NOT ALWAYS POSSIBLE, MRS PASTERNAK. THE LAW MUST COME FIRST.
YOU'LL EXCUSE ME SAYING SO, SIR, BUT YOU OWE HER THAT MUCH. AFTER WHAT HAPPENED TO MR RICO. . .
WHO KILLED DADDY, UNCLE JOE? WAS HE A BAD MAN?
NO, CHILD. HE WAS...JUST DOING HIS JOB.
HOW CAN I TELL HER IT WAS ME WHO KILLED HER DADDY? RICO, MY BROTHER . . .
YOU SENT ME TO TITAN, BROTHER JOE – YOU TURNED ME INTO A FREAK! NOW YOU'RE GONNA PAY FOR IT!
A JUDGE THAT GOES WRONG HAS GOT TO BE PUNISHED! DON'T MAKE ME KILL YOU!
2074
DRAW, I SAID – AAAGH!
YOU DON'T KISS ME AND HUG ME VERY MUCH, BUT I KNOW THAT'S JUST YOUR WAY. I LOVE YOU, UNCLE JOE! YOU'RE MY DADDY NOW!
NO, PLEASE NOT THAT! NOT AFTER WHAT I DID!

DREDD STOPPED HIS BIKE ON SIGMA STREET —
LOOKS QUIET ENOUGH... BUT HARRY C WILL BE IN THERE. CRACKPOTS LIKE HIM LOVE TO BE IN AT THE KILL !
HARRY CARMEN WAS WAITING WITH THE DOOR OPEN...
WELCOME, DREDDY. I'VE BEEN EXPECTING YOU !
UNCLE JOE !
GOTTA WATCH FOR TRAPS. HARRY C IS A WIZARD WITH ELECTRONICS !
ZAP!
I THOUGHT SO !
AAH-ANKLE TRAP!
SNAP!
I KNEW THE LASER WOULDN'T GET YOU, DREDDY. NOW WE CAN PROCEED WITH THE ENTERTAINMENT !
BLADE
U-UNCLE JOE! THE BLADE IS MOVING !
ITS RATE OF DESCENT IS LINKED DIRECTLY TO THE CHILD'S HEART BEAT. AT HER PRESENT PULSE RATE SHE WILL BE DEAD IN THREE MINUTES! ANY INTERFERENCE WITH THE EQUIPMENT WILL MERELY SPEED IT UP !

DAMN YOU, HARRY! RELEASE HER—OR SO HELP ME, I'LL KILL YOU!
I'VE HAD SIX YEARS TO PLAN MY REVENGE, DREDD. SIX YEARS TO FIND THE THING THAT'LL HURT YOU MOST—THE LITTLE GIRL YOU FEEL SO GUILTY ABOUT!
YOU KILLED HER FATHER, DREDD—AND NOW **SHE'S** GOING TO DIE BECAUSE OF YOU! ***AND YOU'RE GOING TO WATCH EVERY SECOND!***
YOU WON'T KILL ME, DREDD. YOU ALWAYS *STICK* TO THE ***LAW BOOKS***, AN' THEY SAY YOU CAN ONLY KILL ME IF IT'LL HELP SAVE A LIFE—WHICH IT WON'T!

AT LEAST **YOU** WON'T HAVE THE PLEASURE OF WATCHING, HARRY! ***STUN SHOT!***
AAAH!

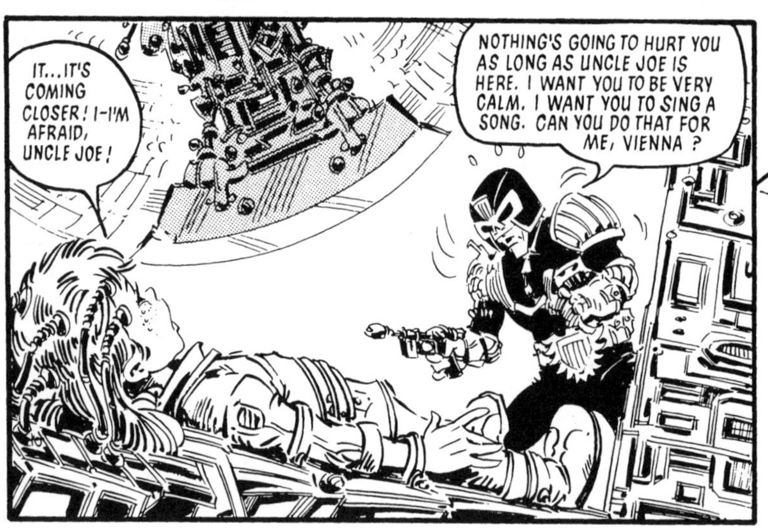
IT...IT'S COMING CLOSER! I-I'M AFRAID, UNCLE JOE!
NOTHING'S GOING TO HURT YOU AS LONG AS UNCLE JOE IS HERE. I WANT YOU TO BE VERY CALM. I WANT YOU TO SING A SONG. CAN YOU DO THAT FOR ME, VIENNA?

YES, UNCLE JOE.
♫ TWINKLE, TWINKLE, L-LITTLE STAR, HOW I WONDER WHERE YOU ARE...♫

UP ABOVE THE WORLD SO HIGH...
THE LESS AFRAID SHE IS, THE SLOWER HER HEART BEATS. BLAST THIS METAL! IT WON'T BREAK!
DREDD STRETCHED FORWARD...
I CAN SEE THE CONTROLS REFLECTED IN THE WALL PANEL. TIME'S RUNNING OUT — GOTTA MAKE THIS SHOT COUNT!
RICOCHET!
ZIIT!
SPANG!
TWAK!
MANACLE RETRACT
CLICK!
U-UNCLE JOE! IT-IT'S SO CLOSE!
I'M FREE!
DREDD RIPPED AT THE STRAPS WITH HIS KNIFE, AND —
CHUNK!
YOU'RE SAFE, DARLING! THANK DOKK, YOU'RE SAFE!
THE ONE TIME IN MY LIFE I WANT TO KILL SOMEONE! BUT YOU'RE RIGHT, HARRY — I WON'T. INSTEAD, I'M GOING TO PUT YOU OUT OF HARM'S WAY FOR THE REST OF YOUR LIFE!

DREDD SAW HIS PRISONER IN CUSTODY, THEN TOOK VIENNA HOME...
UNCLE JOE, WAS IT TRUE WHAT THAT BAD MAN SAID? DID YOU...DID YOU REALLY KILL MY DADDY?
I'M... AFRAID SO, DARLING.
IF... IF YOU KILLED DADDY, THEN... THEN YOU MUST HAVE HAD A GOOD REASON. I STILL LOVE YOU, UNCLE JOE.
2000 A.D.
Credit Card:
SCRIPT ROBOT JOHN HOWARD
ART ROBOT IAN GIBSON
LETTERING ROBOT TOM FRAME
COMPU-73E
VIENNA WAS PUT TO BED —
WELL, THIS HAS BEEN A FINE HOWDEDO! I HOPE IT'S SHOWN YOU YOUR DUTY, SIR. VIENNA WILL BE SEEING MORE OF YOU NOW, EH?
NO, MRS PASTERNAK. I INTEND TO SEE LESS OF MY NIECE. YOU MUST HELP HER TO STOP LOVING ME!
REALLY! I ALWAYS KNEW YOU WERE A COLD ONE — BUT THIS! YOU'VE NO HEART AT ALL, JOE DREDD! YOU-YOU'RE JUST A SOULLESS MACHINE!
YOU DON'T UNDERSTAND, MRS PASTERNAK. I'M A JUDGE — SOMEDAY I, TOO, WILL BE KILLED. VIENNA COULDN'T TAKE THAT AGAIN, NOT A SECOND TIME.
SHE'S SUFFERED ENOUGH BECAUSE OF ME. LET IT END HERE.
NEXT. PROG: CITYBLOCK*1

LOOK OUT, LAWBREAKERS! IT'S
JUDGE DREDD
HYPER-COP!
2000 A.D. Credit Card:
SCRIPT ROBOT JOHN HOWARD
ART ROBOT RON SMITH
LETTERING ROBOT TOM FRAME
COMPU-73E
EVERY MONDAY JUDGE DREDD'S ROBOSERVANT WALTER PAYS A VISIT TO THE LOCAL HYPER-LAUNDRY—
MEGA-CITY WASHIN
GOSH, IT'S THE FAMOUS WALTER!
WALTER PUT JUDGE DWEDD'S NAME ON ALL HIS CLOTHES. WHEN OTHER WOBOSERVANTS SEE HE IS THE GWEAT JUDGE'S WOBOT, WALTER FEEL PWOUD AS PUNCH!
SOAPY 7
SPIKE
JUDGE DREDD
I'M WALTER TRY ME
LAUNDRY BAG
MY MASTER IS ONLY AN INSURANCE SALESMAN. IT MUST BE VERY EXCITING BEING JUDGE DREDD'S ROBOT.
THAT'S TWUE. IT TAKES A PWETTY WUFF AND WEADY WOBOT TO BE JUDGE DWEDD'S DWOID. WALTER HAS BEEN IN SOME TIGHT SCWAPES.
IN FACT, WALTER JUST HAPPEN TO BWING HIS SCWAPBOOK— WOULD YOU LIKE TO SEE IT?
YOU BET, WALTER!
BOB
SCRAPBOOK
FREEDOM
I'M WALTER TRY ME
NOW THIS PHOTOGWAPH WAS TAKEN JUST AFTER THE WOBOT WAR, WHEN WALTER WAS GIVEN HIS FWEEDOM FOR HELPING JUDGE DWEDD SAVE MEGA-CITY ONE.

DREDD'S ROBOT SENT TO JAIL
ONE MONTH IN SING-SING. WALTER, JUDGE DREDD'S ... INCARCERATED BY ... OF JUDGE DR...
WOW - A CON-DROID! BUT I'LL BET JUDGE DREDD SOON GOT YOU OUT!
YOU CWACKPOT WOBOT! IT WAS JUDGE DWEDD WHO SENT WALTER TO PWISON!
TELL US ABOUT IT, WALTER.
PLEASE! PLEASE!
WELL, IT HAPPEN NOT LONG AFTER THE WOBOT WAR. EVEN THOUGH WALTER WAS A FWEE WOBOT, HE WAS STILL JUDGE DWEDD'S DEVOTED —AND UNPAID— SERVANT...
"AS WALTER WEMEMBER, THERE WAS A WOBBEWY AT THE CWEDIT BANK THAT DAY. JUDGE DWEDD HAD TWAPPED THE CWOOKS INSIDE — "
CREDIT BANK
I'VE BWOUGHT YOUR LUNCH, JUDGE DWEDD. IT'S SYNTHI-VEG SOUP FOR STARTERS.
JUDGE DREDD
WHAT-OH, WALTER...
WATCH THAT DOOR, MASON! THERE'S SOMEONE COMING OUT!
IT'S ONE OF THE HOSTAGES!
BLAM!
BAM!
GOTTA GET —
AAAGH!

LET THAT BE A WARNING, DREDD! ONE HOSTAGE DIES EVERY TEN MINUTES UNTIL YOU GIVE US A SAFE RIDE OUTA HERE!
LIKE HELL I WILL!
BOOM! CRASH! BLAM!
IT'S TIME I GOT TOUGH WITH THESE MURDERERS!
DREDD'S GOING INTO THE NEXT BUILDING!
COME BACK HERE, ROBOT!
SMASH
JUDGE DWEDD HASN'T FINISHED HIS LUNCH! IT IS WALTER'S DUTY TO TAKE IT TO HIM!
"INSIDE, JUDGE DWEDD'S SUPER BWAIN HAD FIGURED OUT A PLAN..."
BIKE CANNON TO NARROW BEAM, CONTINUOUS FIRE! THE BANK VAULT SHOULD BE JUST BEHIND THIS WALL - IT'S THE LAST PLACE THEY'D EXPECT ME TO COME FROM!
BLAST!
YOO HOO, JUDGE DWEDD! WALTER HAS BWOUGHT THE WEST OF YOUR LUNCH!
WALTER! DROKK IT, ROBOT, GO HOME! CAN'T YOU SEE I'M IN THE MIDDLE OF A CASE!
WITH GWEAT WESPECT, MASTER, IT IS A JUDGE'S DUTY TO KEEP HIS STWENGTH UP. AS YOU CAN SEE ON MY PWINTOUT, WALTER'S CAREFULLY PWEPARED MEALS PWOVIDE ALL THE NUTWITION A SUPER-ACTIVE JUDGE NEEDS.
CALORIES NUT: VALUE %
SOUP 170 99
STEW 712 91
DESERT 475 92
"A DUTIFUL WOBOT SHOULD KNOW HOW TO GET HIS OWN WAY..."
THERE'S CUSTARD CWEAM PIE TO FOLLOW.
OH, FOR HEAVEN'S SAKE!
RROAR-R-RRR!
ZIZZZ-ZZZZ!

"JUDGE DWEDD WOARED OUT OF THE VAULT *BLASTING* –"
AAGH!
"NO CWOOK IN THE WORLD CAN LIVE WITH MY MASTER. HE'S A *HEWO* THWOO AND THWOO!"
THUD!
FTOM!
THANK GOD YOU'RE HERE, JUDGE DREDD!
BE CAREFUL, WOMAN –
UUH!
I GOT YOU NOW, DREDD! MAYBE THOSE OTHER JUDGES WILL THINK DIFFERENT ABOUT LETTING US GO WHEN WE THROW *YOUR* BODY OUT!

I'VE BWOUGHT YOUR DESSERT, JUDGE DW— OH, CWIPES!
AHH – I CAN'T SEE!
SPLURGE
GOOD WORK, WALTER!
" JUDGE DWEDD SEIZED HIS OPPORTUNITY – "
UUUGH!
KAPOW!
" JUDGE DWEDD GAVE THE CWOOKS LONG SENTENCES. HE IS A VEWY TOUGH MAN... "
I'M GRATEFUL FOR YOUR HELP, WALTER – BUT IN DOING SO, YOU BROKE THE LAW. YOU STRUCK A HUMAN.
THE CUSTARD CWEAM PIE! OH, CWIPES, WALTER NEVER THOUGHT –
POLICE V
THE ROBOT LAWS ARE VERY STRICT, WALTER. BUT AS YOU ARE A FREE ROBOT, THE NORMAL PENALTIES DO NOT APPLY. STILL, I HAVE NO ALTERNATIVE BUT TO SENTENCE YOU TO ONE MONTH IN A HUMAN PRISON!
I UNDERSTAND, JUDGE DWEDD! YOU MUST MAKE AN EXAMPLE OF FAITHFUL WALTER. WALTER IS WILLING!
THAT ROBOT SAVED YOUR LIFE – YOU CAN'T SEND HIM TO JAIL! IT'S INHUMAN!
GO GO
JUDGE DWEDD IS THE BEST JUDGE IN MEGA-CITY ONE AND I'LL THANK YOU NOT TO CWITICISE! IF HE GIVES WALTER PWISON SENTENCE, THEN BAD WALTER DESERVE IT!

WALTER WILL PWEPARE A *PWOPER DIET SHEET* FOR YOU BEFORE HE GO TO PWISON. OTHERWISE MAWIA WILL BE STUFFING YOU WITH ALL THAT GWEASY ITALIAN FOOD!
"JUDGE DWEDD WAS VEWY KIND. HE SENT WALTER TO *NEW SING-SING*, THAT NICE OLD-FASHIONED PWISON..."
A NEW CELL-MATE FOR YOU, BUCK. BETTER TREAT HIM GOOD — HE'S JUDGE DREDD'S ROBOT!
218
HOLY HECK, WHY ME? DREDD'S THE RAT THAT *PUT* ME IN HERE!
BET YOU'RE MAD AT OLD DREDDY, EH, WALT?
ON THE CONTWAWY, I'M VEWY *PWOUD* OF HIM! HE WOULD HAVE FAILED IN HIS DUTY IF HE HADN'T AWWESTED WALTER FOR HIS WICKED CWIME!
DREDD
"WALTER'S CELL-MATE DIDN'T SEEM TO LIKE WALTER. WALTER WAS ALWAYS *VEWY FWIENDLY* TO HIM, SO IT IS HARD TO UNDERSTAND—"
NOW I LAY ME DOWN TO SLEEP, I PWAY THE LORD JUDGE DWEDD TO KEEP. FEED HIM WIGHT, NO STARCH OR FAT, KEEP HIM WELL TILL WALT GET BACK.
NO! NO! I CAN'T TAKE ANY MORE!
GET ME OUTA HERE! PUT ME IN *SOLITARY*— *ANYWHERE*!
JUST GET ME AWAY FROM THAT DREDD-LOVING ROBOT!
AFTER WALTER WAS WELEASED, JUDGE DWEDD TOOK HIM STWAIGHT BACK. ALL WAS FORGIVEN. JUDGE DWEDD EVEN SEEMED A LITTLE *PLEASED* TO SEE WALTER. THAT MADE WALTER VEWY HAPPY!
GEE, WALT, I ENJOYED THAT STORY.
GOSH, I DON'T KNOW IF I'D LIKE TO BELONG TO JUDGE DREDD AFTER ALL!
YEAH! IT TAKES A *SPECIAL* KIND OF ROBOT...
NEXT PROG: THE FOREVER CRIMES!

ZARJAZ 3RD BIRTHDAY ISSUE!
Malaysia $1.00
New Zealand 35c
Australia 35c
South Africa 35c
Mercury 17g
Venus 10g
Mars 15g
Asteroid Belt 20g
Saturn 84g
Neptune 87g
Pluto 93g
12p EARTH MONEY
2000 AD
AND TORNADO
15 MAR 80
PROG 156
IN ORBIT EVERY MONDAY
HUGE COMPETITION INSIDE!
80 THUR FLASH PISTOLS TO BE WON!
AS DISTRIBUTED BY MORRIS VULCAN
PLUS
* ROBOTS!
* VAMPIRES!
* ALIENS!
* SPACE-HEROES!
* FEATURES!
AND...
HAVE YOU SEEN THIS BOY?
THE JUDGE CHILD —A GREAT NEW JUDGE DREDD EPIC STARTS INSIDE—IN COLOUR!

FIND THE CHILD WHO BEARS THE EAGLE MARK
ONLY HE CAN SAVE MEGA-CITY ONE !
MUTIE SLAVERS ! THEY COU
THE ONES I'M AFTER
DREDD

JUDGE DREDD IN
THE JUDGE CHILD
SCRIPT ROBOT JOHN HOWARD
ART ROBOT BRIAN BOLLAND
LETTERING ROBOT TOM FRAME

IN THE CURSED EARTH – THE NUCLEAR WASTELAND BEYOND MEGA-CITY ONE – ISOLATED MUTANT DOMESTEADS WERE EASY PICKINGS FOR BANDS OF VICIOUS SLAVETRADERS...

EASY PICKINGS... UNLESS JUDGE DREDD HAPPENED TO BE AROUND!

MUTIE HAVEN

A JUDGE!

YOU SLAVERS GOT A CHOICE! SURRENDER OR DIE!

AAGH!
DEATH IT IS THEN!
AAARGH!
WHIP'S GOT ME! UUH!
SSNAP!
YOU'RE GONNA GET THE SANDPAPER TREATMENT, LAWMAN!
GOTTA TURN—
GEDDOWN, CREEP!
AHH!
HRRHEEIE!
BEWARE! SULFER SAND

SULPHUR SAND — IT'S S-SUCKING ME IN! HELP ME, JUDGE!
THAT ALL DEPENDS ON THE ANSWERS YOU GIVE ME...

ANSWERS? ANSWERS TO WHAT, DROKK YA?

SIX MONTHS AGO SLAVERS ATTACKED A SETTLEMENT EAST OF HERE. THIS BOY, OWEN KRYSLER, WAS TAKEN. I WANT THAT BOY!

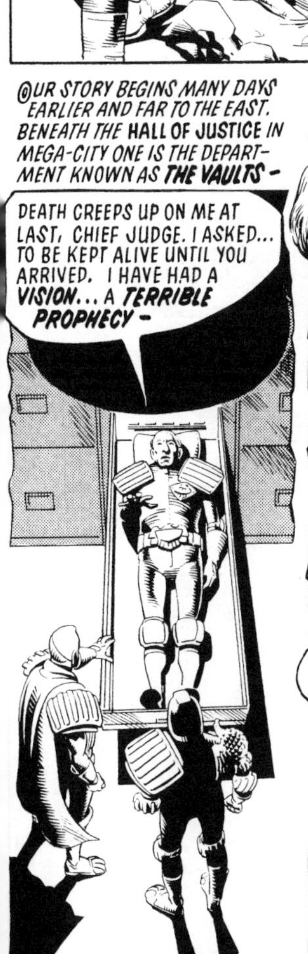
OUR STORY BEGINS MANY DAYS EARLIER AND FAR TO THE EAST. BENEATH THE HALL OF JUSTICE IN MEGA-CITY ONE IS THE DEPARTMENT KNOWN AS THE VAULTS-
DEATH CREEPS UP ON ME AT LAST, CHIEF JUDGE. I ASKED... TO BE KEPT ALIVE UNTIL YOU ARRIVED. I HAVE HAD A VISION... A TERRIBLE PROPHECY-

JUDGE FEYY WAS THE CITY'S OLDEST PRE-COG. HIS VISIONS OF THE FUTURE WERE 88.8% ACCURATE —
I SAW A WAR MORE GHASTLY THAN ANY WE HAVE KNOWN. I SAW OUR CITY DESTROYED — AND FROM THE DESTRUCTION FOUL CREATURES ROSE TO PREY ON THE SURVIVORS...!
THIS WILL HAPPEN IN THE YEAR 2120.

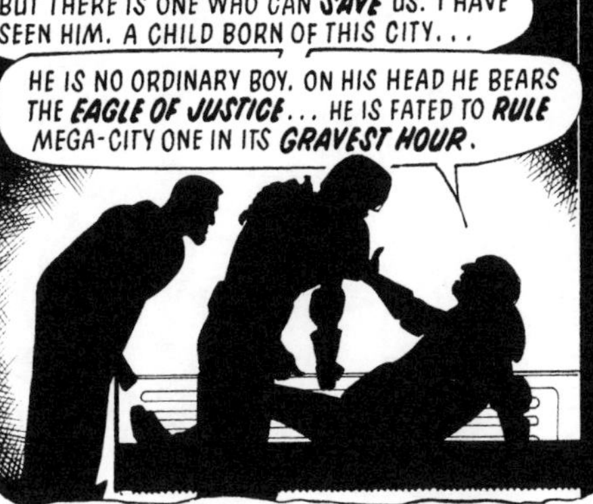
BUT THERE IS ONE WHO CAN SAVE US. I HAVE SEEN HIM. A CHILD BORN OF THIS CITY...
HE IS NO ORDINARY BOY. ON HIS HEAD HE BEARS THE EAGLE OF JUSTICE... HE IS FATED TO RULE MEGA-CITY ONE IN ITS GRAVEST HOUR.

I HAVE ONLY A NAME — OWEN KRYSLER. HE CAN GUIDE US THROUGH THE DARKNESS. FIND HIM —
FIND THE JUDGE CHILD!

MANY OF OUR PRE-COGS HAVE PREDICTED A TIME OF CRISIS IN THE EARLY 'TWENTIES. THIS IS THE CLEAREST VISION WE'VE HAD OF IT YET.
THERE ARE 47 OWEN KRYSLERS IN THE CITY. NONE OF THEM FITS JUDGE FEYY'S DESCRIPTION.
DREDD

BUT THERE WAS **ONE OTHER** OWEN KRYSLER. HE LEFT THE CITY FOUR YEARS AGO WITH HIS PARENTS TO SETTLE IN THE NEW MUTIELAND TERRITORIES. THAT'S ALL WE KNOW.
AND YOU WANT ME TO CHECK ON HIM...?

IT MIGHT BE A WILD GOOSE CHASE — JUDGE FEYY COULD BE **WRONG**. BUT WE CAN'T TAKE THE CHANCE. THE BOY COULD BE THE ONLY HOPE FOR MEGA-CITY ONE!

IT WAS MANY DAYS LATER WHEN JUDGE DREDD FOUND THE SETTLEMENT...
DROKK! WHAT'S HAPPENED HERE?
SLIM'S SALOON

SLAVERS GOT 'EM! TOOK WHAT THEY WANTED AND STRUNG UP THE REST — ALL 'CEPT ME! SAID I WAS SO **UGLY**, THE CRUELLEST THING WAS TO LET ME LIVE! RECKON THEY WAS RIGHT, TOO!
I'M LOOKING FOR PEOPLE CALLED KRYSLER.

YOU COME TO THE RIGHT PLACE, JUDGE. **THAT'S** THE KRYSLERS! LOVELY COUPLE, AIN'T THEY?
THE BOY — WHAT HAPPENED TO HIM?
SLAVERS TOOK HIM!
HARWOOD'S STORE

DREDD FOUND THE HOLOGRAM INSIDE THE HOUSE —
A BIRTHMARK LIKE THE EAGLE OF JUSTICE! ***IT'S HIM!***

NOW, A WEEK LATER, DREDD HAD LOCATED THE GROUP OF SLAVERS –
THAT MARK! YEAH, I RECOGNISE THE KID – I REMEMBER HIM GOOD! HE WAS A REAL STRANGE ONE...

THE KID DIDN'T CRY WHEN WE STRUNG UP HIS MA AN' PA! DIDN'T MAKE NO FUSS AT ALL! IT WAS LIKE HE KNEW IT WOULD HAPPEN!
I MUST GO ON MY JOURNEY NOW. GOODBYE, MOTHER. GOODBYE, FATHER. WE WILL MEET AGAIN IN ANOTHER PLACE.
PROV

AND THE BOY?
WE THOUGHT WE'D GET A GOOD PRICE FOR A STRANGE KID LIKE THAT. SOME OF THE GUYS TOOK HIM TO THE SLAVE MARKET IN NEUTRON FLATS. THAT'S ALL I KNOW!

HE'S ALL YOURS, BOYS!
HEY, WAIT! YOU PROMISED!
DREDD

I KEPT MY PROMISE. YOU'RE OUT OF THE SULPHUR SAND.
YOU'RE GONNA DANGLE, SLAVER!
JUST LIKE ALL YOUR INNOCENT VICTIMS!

DREDD REPAIRED HIS BIKE AND SENT OFF A MESSAGE POD –

RADIO CONTACT'S IMPOSSIBLE THROUGH THE CURSED EARTH. THE POD'LL CARRY WORD BACK TO MEGA-CITY ONE.

MUTIE HAVEN
THE MORE I LEARN OF THIS BOY, THE MORE CERTAIN I BECOME THAT HE IS THE JUDGE CHILD. I WON'T REST UNTIL I'VE FOUND HIM!
NEXT PROG: "WHAT AM I BID FOR JUDGE DREDD!?"

JUDGE DREDD
THE JUDGE CHILD
PART 2
DISASTER HAD BEEN PREDICTED FOR MEGA-CITY ONE UNLESS THE BOY WITH THE EAGLE MARK – THE JUDGE CHILD – CAN BE BROUGHT BACK TO RULE THE CITY. IN THE CURSED EARTH, JUDGE DREDD IS SEARCHING FOR THE BOY. THE TRAIL LEADS TO THE SLAVE MARKET IN THE TOWN OF NEUTRON FLATS –
NEUTRON FLAT
SLAVE MARKE
THE NEXT ITEM – ONE MEGA-CITY JUDGE! IN PRIME CONDITION! NO PREVIOUS OWNER!
WHAT AM I BID FOR JUDGE DREDD?
FIFTY GOLD PIECES!
SIXTY!
BUY HIM FOR ME, DEAR! I MUST OWN MY OWN JUDGE!
2000 A.D.
Credit Card:
SCRIPT ROBOT JOHN HOWARD
ART ROBOT RON SMITH
LETTERING ROBOT TOM FRAME
COMPU·73E

EARLIER THAT DAY DREDD, DISGUISED BY A RADIATION CLOAK, RODE INTO NEUTRON FLATS —
NEUTRON FLATS IS THE BIGGEST SLAVE MARKET IN MUTIELAND. WITHOUT LAW, PEOPLE SOON FALL BACK INTO THE OLD EVILS!
TAKEAWAY
TOP QUALITY! SLAVING KIT
WILSONS MUTIE SLAVE DEPT
"PROP: MAK'S" TASTEEFRY
TAKE HOME TWO TODAY
WHAT AM I BID FOR THIS MUTANT? TOBY'S A HANDY MAN TO HAVE AROUND!
SAVE ME, BROTHER! YOU'RE A RELIGIOUS MAN! TELL THEM THEY CAN'T SELL ME LIKE A-AN ANIMAL!
TEN GOLD PIECES!
SOLD TO BROTHER FRYPAN OF THE BROTHERHOOD OF TRASH!
BONG!
HA HA HA HA

THAT'S ALL FOR NOW, FOLKS! SLAVE AUCTION REOPENS RIGHT AFTER LUNCH!
MUTANT PREYING UPON MUTANT! LAW IS BADLY NEEDED HERE. BUT MY MISSION IS TO FIND THE JUDGE CHILD, AND I MUST NOT BE SIDETRACKED...
IN THE AUCTIONEER'S TENT—
CAN'T YOU SEE I'M HAVING LUNCH, STRANGER? COME BACK — HOLY S-SMOKE! IT— IT'S —
JUDGE DREDD'S THE NAME! GIVE ME ANY TROUBLE AND YOU'LL BE SUCKING DUM-DUMS FOR DESSERT!
THE AUCTIONEER CO-OPERATED—
YES, I REMEMBER THE BOY. I SOLD HIM ABOUT SIX MONTHS AGO TO FILMORE FARO! STRANGE KINDA KID — SORT OF PRE-COG, WASN'T HE?
I'LL ASK THE QUESTIONS! WHO'S FARO?
FILMORE FARO, THE GARBAGE KING! HE OWNS BIG GARBAGE MINES WEST OF HERE! THAT'S SOME OF HIS MEN, IN BUYING SLAVES...
THE BROTHERHOOD OF TRASH... STRANGE HOW THE CURSED EARTH THROWS UP THESE CRAZY RELIGIONS!
THEY AIN'T RELIGIOUS. THEY'RE JUST BAD TYPES OUT FOR WHAT THEY CAN GET FROM FARO. HE'S CRAZY AS A COCKROACH! THINKS HE'S SOME KINDA GARBAGE GOD!
TRADING POST
BAR
DANCE HALL
SLAVES
FARO MAY BE CRAZY, BUT HE OWNS TEN THOUSAND SLAVES AND MOST OF THE LAND ROUND MEMPHIS. HE GOT POWER — AND HE DON'T TAKE KINDLY TO LAWMEN!
IF I BLOW THE GAFF TOO SOON, I'LL ENDANGER THE BOY. BUT THERE'S ONE WAY OF GETTING INTO FARO'S TERRITORY WITHOUT ANY SUSPICION...
OUTSIDE, DREDD SPOKE TO HIS BIKE COMPUTER—
WAIT WEST OF TOWN. FOLLOW ME AT A DISTANCE OF TWO MILES. DON'T APPROACH UNLESS I SIGNAL!
WILCO, JUDGE DREDD.

THE AFTERNOON'S AUCTION BEGAN WITH A SHOCK SPECIAL OFFER –
LADIES, GENTLEMEN AND MUTIES! OSSIE'S SLAVE MART IS PROUD TO ANNOUNCE A DELIVERY OF GOODS ALL THE WAY FROM MEGA-CITY ONE! WHAT AM I BID FOR JUDGE DREDD?
PROP: MAKS
TASTEEFRY
SLAVES
MUTIES
NORMS
Z'SCO DANCE HALL
HE'S IN PRIME CONDITION, FOLKS! LOWER THAT JAW, BOY! LET THE CUSTOMERS SEE THOSE TEETH!
CUT THE WISE STUFF! MESS THIS UP AND I'LL BOOT YOUR HEAD!
THREE-TEN!
THREE-TWENTY!
THREE HUNDRED-FIFTY!
TOO MUCH! THREE HUNDRED'S MY LIMIT!
DROKK!
THE LITTLE RUNT'S GETTING TOO GREEDY!
CRUNCH!
AH! IN VIEW OF THE – OW! OOH! – SPECIAL DIFFICULTY OF HANDLING THIS SLAVE, I CAN'T LET HIM GO FOR MORE THAN THREE HUNDRED!
BONG!
SOLD TO THE BROTHERHOOD OF TRASH!
NEXT DAY, THE BROTHERHOOD BROUGHT THEIR SLAVES INTO FARO'S TERRITORY –
WELCOME, BROTHERS! BLESSED BE THE NAME OF TRASH! SACRED BE THE NAME OF RUBBISH!
GARBAGE TO YOU, TOO, BROTHER!

THAT'S ONE OF FARO'S GARBAGE MINES! IT USED TO BE A BIG TOWN BUT DURING THE WAR IT GOT COVERED OVER BY RADIOACTIVE DUST!
THE DUST PRESERVED EVERYTHING IN THE TOWN! NOW IT'S SAFE AND FARO'S MADE A FORTUNE DIGGING IT UP AND SELLING IT TO RICH COLLECTORS AS ANTIQUES!
ALL THAT PRE-WAR JUNK IS PRICELESS NOW! SHOOT! YOU CAN GET FIFTY GOLD PIECES FOR AN OLD TIN CAN!
WE'VE STRUCK A RICH GARBAGE SEAM!
THE INFORMATION CAME FROM ONE OF THE OTHER CAPTIVES —
BREWSTER ONELUG'S THE NAME! I USED TO BE FARO'S SLAVE, BUT I GOT AWAY. NOW THEY CAUGHT ME AGAIN! IT AIN'T FAIR, JUDGE. ONE DOSE OF FARO IS ENOUGH FOR ANY MAN!
I'M GLAD I'VE GOT A LITTLE INSURANCE!
FARO
WOULD YA LOOK AT THAT! A BIKE WITHOUT A RIDER!
HALT! HECK, THAT SOUNDS DUMB! HOW DO YA THREATEN A MACHINE?
MAYBE WE OUGHTA SPEAK TO IT IN BIKE... PHUT, PHUT, PHUT! THAT MEANS STOP!
YEAH! HA, HA! VROOM VROOOM! THAT MEANS SCRAM OR WE OPEN FIRE!
BLAM! BAM
THAT MEANS DROP DEAD. THANK YOU.

AN HOUR LATER, THE SLAVE CARAVAN HALTED –
OUT, YOU DOGS! IT'S TIME TO EARN YOUR KEEP!
A HUGE PROCESSION WAS CROSSING THE CURSED EARTH –
DROKK! IT'S LIKE SOMETHING OUT OF ANCIENT EGYPT!
JOIN IN, DOGS! FARO'S HEAD MUST BE IN MEMPHIS BY MORNING!
SO THAT'S FARO! HE LOOKS INSANE!
HE IS! HE THINKS HE'S DESCENDED FROM THE ANCIENT PHARAOHS! HE USES HIS FORTUNE BUILDING MONUMENTS TO HIMSELF!
IF YOU THINK THIS IS BAD, WAIT'LL YOU GET A LOAD OF MEMPHIS!
BY DAWN, THE STRANGE PROCESSION WAS IN SIGHT OF THE PLACE WHERE ONCE THE CITY OF MEMPHIS HAD STOOD –
SEE WHAT I MEAN? FARO AND HIS PYRAMIDS! HE'S A NUT!
A FIVE-STAR KOOK! IF THE JUDGE CHILD IS IN FARO'S HANDS, I FEAR FOR HIM!
NEXT PROG: TEMPLE OF THE GARBAGE GOD!

JUDGE DREDD
THE JUDGE CHILD
PART 3
DISASTER HAS BEEN PREDICTED FOR MEGA-CITY ONE UNLESS THE BOY WITH THE EAGLE MARK — THE JUDGE CHILD — CAN BE BROUGHT BACK TO RULE THE CITY. ON THE BOY'S TRAIL, JUDGE DREDD SELLS HIMSELF AS A SLAVE IN ORDER TO ENTER THE TERRITORY OF THE MADMAN, FILMORE FARO, WHO HAS BOUGHT THE JUDGE CHILD —
JUDGE
BEHOLD THE HEAD OF FARO! BRING IT TO THE HOLY SEPULCHRE!
DREDD

2000 A.D.
Credit Card:
SCRIPT ROBOT JOHN HOWARD
ART ROBOT RON SMITH
LETTERING ROBOT TOM FRAME
COMPU·73E

FARO'S **TOMB** IS READY! A FITTING RESTING PLACE FOR A **GOD**!

FARO'S GREAT, WE CAN'T DENY IT! WITH THIS TRASH WE SANCTIFY IT!

FARO
MEMPHIS CITY DUMP
LOWLY MORTALS! I STAND BEFORE YOU A GOD! YES, A GOD!
HAVE I NOT BUILT MONUMENTS EVEN GREATER THAN THE ANCIENT GODS? DO I NOT HAVE THE POWER OF LIFE AND DEATH OVER THOUSANDS OF YOU?
IS NOT MY GARBAGE FINE?
THE BROTHERHOOD OF TRASH ARE JUST BAD TYPES OUT FOR WHAT THEY CAN GET FROM FARO! HE'S THE CRAZY ONE! LOOK!
GRIEF! THE MAN'S A WALKING HEAP OF GARBAGE!
THAT GARBAGE IS WORTH MILLIONS!
FARO HAD BECOME RICH SELLING PRE-WAR GARBAGE TO COLLECTORS AS PRICELESS ANTIQUES. NOW POWER HAD TWISTED HIS MIND –
I, FILMORE FARO, LAST IN THE LINE OF THE ANCIENT PHARAOHS –
HE WAS A CHEAP HUSTLER FROM TEXAS CITY TILL HE HIT ON HIS GARBAGE RACKET!
I AM THE GARBAGE GOD!
HE'S STARK STARING MAD!
I GO NOW TO PREPARE FOR DEATH! TONIGHT THE GARBAGE GOD ASCENDS TO HIS PLACE ON HIGH! THOSE OLD GODS WON'T KNOW WHAT HIT THEM!
WHAT MAKES FARO THINK HE'S GOING TO DIE TONIGHT?
BIRD BOY HAS PREDICTED IT, AND HE IS NEVER WRONG. HE SEES THE FUTURE.
BIRD BOY! DOES HE HAVE A MARK – LIKE AN EAGLE?
THAT IS HIM! HE LIVES YONDER, IN FARO'S NEEDLE! WHEN FARO DIES TONIGHT, BIRD BOY WILL BE KILLED TO ACT AS HIS GUIDE IN THE SPIRIT WORLD!
I'VE FOUND THE JUDGE CHILD – AND NOT BEFORE TIME! GOT TO WORK FAST –

A SMALL TRANSMITTER WAS CONCEALED BENEATH A STRIP OF SYNTHI-SKIN ON DREDD'S ARM –
DREDD'S BIKE, ON COMPUTER CONTROL, WAITED A SAFE DISTANCE AWAY –
I WANT A DIVERSION! CLOSE IN AND OPEN UP WITH BIKE CANNON! MAINTAIN FIRE FOR TWO MINUTES, THEN SCRAM!
WILCO, JUDGE DREDD.
IT CAME IN WITH SIREN WAILING –
HOLY MOSES! LOOK OUT!
BLAM!
BLAM!
OOAAAAAOOOOOAAAAOOOO
EACH SHOT WAS DELIBERATELY OFF-TARGET –
RRR-RATTA-TAT-TAT
IT'S A GHOST RIDER COME TO PUNISH US FOR OUR WICKEDNESS!
THE BROTHERS WERE DRAWN TOWARDS THE TROUBLE –
NOT YOU, GARBAGE BOY!
FWAK!!
AAAAAGH!!

ALL CLEAR!
UNDRESS THAT CREEP AND DITCH HIM SOMEWHERE!

AS DREDD'S BIKE SPED OFF, THE NEW "BROTHER MONKEYWRENCH" ENTERED THE **TEMPLE OF TRASH** -

YOUR BURIAL SHROUD IS READY, FARO! MADE ENTIRELY OF PRICELESS **RING-PULL TABS**, AS YOU ORDERED!
TEN WAGON-LOADS OF BEST GARBAGE ARE COMING IN FROM THE MINES!
EXCELLENT! I WILL TAKE MY WORLDLY FORTUNE **WITH ME** TO THE SPIRIT WORLD!

DREDD HEADED FOR FARO'S NEEDLE -
I'M GOING TO PREPARE THE BOY FOR THE FUNERAL.
PASS, BROTHER BUNSEN!

SO IT'S TIME. YOU'VE BROUGHT THE DRUG...
NO USE HIDING IT FROM YOU, IS THERE, KID? YOU KNOW **EVERYTHING**!

NOT EVERYTHING. I SEE THE NEEDLE, BUT THEN... ONLY **SHADOWS**...

PERHAPS IT IS... DEATH...

HOLD IT, BROTHER MONKEYWRENCH! ONLY BROTHER BUNSEN SEES BIRD BOY WITHOUT THE PASSWORD!
PASSWORD — YEAH... I'M A LITTLE **SHORT** OF WORDS TODAY, FELLAS —

WILL **THIS** DO?

DREDD HID THE BODIES, THEN —
GUNFIRE WILL GIVE THE GAME AWAY! HAVE TO BLUFF THIS OTHER CREEP —

BROTHER BUNSEN! TROUBLE WITH SOME OF THE SLAVES! FARO WANTS YOU QUICK!
CAN'T THAT IDIOT HANDLE THINGS HIMSELF? OKAY! LOOK AFTER THE KID, WILL YA?

WORKED LIKE A CHARM! AND THAT'S THE BOY, ALL RIGHT! HARD TO BELIEVE I'VE FOUND HIM. IT'S BEEN ALMOST **TOO** EASY —

WHAT THE —? **NEEDLE!**

THE KID DOESN'T TELL ME EVERYTHING — BUT SOMETIMES HE TALKS IN HIS SLEEP! HE HAPPENED TO MENTION YOU MIGHT BE CALLIN', BROTHER JUDGE!
UUUUH...

YOU DESERVE SOME KINDA **REWARD** FOR YOUR TROUBLE — AN' I THINK I KNOW JUST THE THING!
NEXT PROG: SACRIFICE TO THE GARBAGE GOD!

JUDGE DREDD
JUDGE
THE JUDGE CHILD
PART 4
TOMB OF THE GARBAGE GOD!
THE CURSED EARTH HAD NEVER WITNESSED SO INSANE A FUNERAL! FIRST CAME DANCING DERVISHES FROM THE BROTHERHOOD OF TRASH—
BEHIND THEM, TEN SLAVES FOR HUMAN SACRIFICE!

2000 A.D.
Credit Card:
SCRIPT ROBOT JOHN HOWARD
ART ROBOT RON SMITH
LETTERING ROBOT TOM FRAME
COMPU-73E
FARO
...D MUTANTS – LIKENESSES ...NCIENT GODS OF EGYPT – ...E FUNERAL CHARIOT! ...THE TWO GARBAGE-CASKETS –
IN ONE, THE STRANGE CHILD WHO WOULD BE FARO'S GUIDE IN THE SPIRIT WORLD –
MEMPHIS SCRAP Co
IN THE OTHER, GLITTERING IN HIS SHROUD OF FIVE THOUSAND PRICELESS RING-PULL TABS, FILMORE FARO – RULER, MADMAN... GARBAGE GOD!

ON THE TRAIL OF THE JUDGE CHILD, JUDGE DREDD HAS ENTERED THE TERRITORY OF FILMORE FARO IN THE CURSED EARTH. FARO HAD MADE A FORTUNE SELLING PRE-WAR GARBAGE AS ANTIQUES, BUT POWER HAD TWISTED HIS MIND. HE BELIEVED HE WAS DESCENDED FROM THE ANCIENT PHARAOHS — AND THAT TONIGHT HE WOULD ASCEND TO HIS PLACE AMONG THE GODS!
MEMPHIS CITY DUMP
BEHOLD! THE SKIES BURST! IT'S THOSE OTHER GODS — WEEPING! THEY FEAR MY COMING!
THEY CANNOT MATCH THE MAGNIFICENCE OF MY GARBAGE!
MOVE, YOU DOGS! DESTINY AWAITS THE GARBAGE GOD!
KKRACK!
BEHIND THE FUNERAL CHARIOT CAME TEN WAGON-LOADS OF FINEST GARBAGE — THE EARTHLY TREASURE THAT WOULD ACCOMPANY FARO TO THE SPIRIT WORLD.
YOU SLAVES WAIT HERE! WHEN WORD HAS COME THAT FARO AND BIRD BOY ARE DEAD, YOUR THROATS WILL BE CUT. YOUR SPIRITS WILL GUARD FARO'S TOMB FOREVER!
AND IF YOU BELIEVE THAT, YOU'LL BELIEVE ANYTHING!
OUTSIDE, TROUBLE WAS BREWING —
FARO'S GONE! THE BROTHERHOOD OF TRASH DON'T OWN US! WE'RE FREE MEN!
BACK, SCUM! THIS MUTIE MINCER SAYS YOU'RE STILL SLAVES!
RRATTA-TAT-TAT

THE SLAVES ARE GETTING RESTLESS, BROTHER BUNSEN! HEY — YOU'RE LEAVING!
TOO RIGHT! IT'S BEEN A GREAT RACKET, BUT WITHOUT FARO ALL HELL'S GONNA BREAK LOOSE! TAKE MY ADVICE — GRAB WHAT YOU CAN AND BEAT IT WHILE THE GETTING'S GOOD!
BETCHA GOT SOME GOOD GARBAGE IN THE BOX, HUH?
BETTER THAN GARBAGE, SON, THE BEST PRIZE OF ALL!
JUDGE DREDD WAS AMONG THOSE CHOSEN FOR SACRIFICE —
MAYBE WE-WE'LL BE LUCKY AND FARO WON'T DIE...!
NO CHANCE! BIRD BOY PREDICTED IT — HE'S NEVER WRONG!
BIRD BOY IS THE ONE I SEEK — THE JUDGE CHILD! IF I DELAY MUCH LONGER, IT MAY BE TOO LATE!
A STRIP OF SYNTHI-SKIN CONCEALED A MINUTE TRANSMITTER —
HOME IN ON ME, BIKE! STOP FOR NOTHING — THIS IS THE BIG ONE!
DREDD'S BIKE WAS ON COMPUTER CONTROL —
THE GHOST RIDER AGAIN! BLOW HIM AWAY — AAAGH!
OOOOAAAOOOOOAAAAAAAA
BLAM-BAM.
BLAM-BAM.
AAAH!
THIS IS OUR CHANCE!
FREEDOM FOR THE SLAVES!
FTAK! FTAK!
THE STORM THAT HAD BEEN BREWING — ERUPTED!
BAM BAM BAM
DEATH TO THE BROTHERHOOD OF TRASH!
BLAM!

AIEEEE!
ZAT
ZAT
ABOUT TIME! FIX THESE CHAINS!
SPANG!
IN THE INNER SANCTUM–
BROTHER BUNSEN HAS DRUGGED THE BOY WELL. HE WILL FEEL NOTHING WHEN THE SPIKE GOES IN.
JUST YOU REMEMBER TO CLOSE THE LID AS SOON AS I'M DEAD! I DON'T WANT TO BE LEFT WITHOUT MY SPIRIT GUIDE!
HOW WILL I DIE...? WE SHALL SEE! COME, DEATH – I AM READY! IT'S NOT SMART TO KEEP A GARBAGE GOD WAITING!
DEATH CAME!
AAGH!
...BANG!..
BANG! BANG!
DEATH IN BLACK! EXCELLENT! BLACK IS MY FAVOURITE COLOUR!

TAKE ME!
REQUEST GRANTED!
BLAM!
AAAAAAAAAA
I WANT THAT BOY ALIVE, CREEP!
POW!
OKAY! EASY! THE KID DON'T MEAN NOTHING TO ME!
THANK DROKK! I'VE DONE IT!
DREDD

MY GUIDE – YOU WON'T STEAL – MY GUIIEEEEED –
FARO! HE'S STILL ALIVE!
MEMPHIS CITY DUMP
JUDGE CHILD
DREDD

MY GRIEF!
SLAM!

DREDD CARRIED THE BOY'S BODY OUT. BY NOW, THE SLAVES WERE IN CONTROL —
I HAD HIM IN MY GRASP! THE CHILD WHO COULD HAVE SAVED MY CITY — AND I LOST HIM! I'VE FAILED! FAILED!
AND THEN —
THE EAGLE MARK — IT'S RUNNING!
IT'S JUST... MAKE-UP! STOMM! THIS ISN'T THE JUDGE CHILD! SOMEONE'S SUBSTITUTED ANOTHER BOY FOR HIM!
AT ONE OF FARO'S PYRAMIDS, THE BROTHERHOOD OF TRASH WERE BEING GIVEN THEIR LAST RITES —
HAPPY LANDINGS, BROTHER!
PRETTY GOOD, HUH, JUDGE? WE FOUND THEM OLD SKATEBOARDS IN FARO'S GARBAGE VAULTS!
THE ONE THAT LOOKED AFTER THE CHILD — BROTHER BUNSEN... DID YOU FIND HIM?
OOOHH-NOOO-NOO!
NO, WORST LUCK! BROTHER BUNSEN TOOK OFF WITH A BOX OF LOOT BEFORE THE TROUBLE STARTED! A REAL CRAFTY RAT IS BROTHER BUNSEN!
YYYYEEEEOOOWW!
KRUMPH!
CRAFTIER THAN YOU KNOW, BREWSTER. HE'S GOT THE JUDGE CHILD!
NEXT PROG: JUDGE DREDD WALKS TALL IN TEXAS CITY!

IN ORBIT
EVERY
MONDAY
PROG 161
Malaysia $1.00
New Zealand 35c
Australia 35c
South Africa 35c
Mercury 17g
Venus 10g
Mars 15g
Asteroid Belt 20g
Saturn 84g
Neptune 87g
Pluto 93g
12p
EARTH
MONEY
19 APR 80
AND
TORNADO

JUDGE DREDD
JUDGE
THE JUDGE CHILD PART 5
BROTHER DEATH.
---- DREDD'S ROUTE
MEGA-CITY ONE
TEXAS CITY
CURSED EARTH
LAKE LOUISIANA
BLACK ATLANTIC
DISASTER HAS BEEN PREDICTED FOR MEGA-CITY ONE UNLESS THE BOY WITH THE EAGLE MARK – THE JUDGE CHILD – CAN BE BROUGHT BACK TO RULE THE CITY. NOW IN THE HANDS OF THE MONK BROTHER BUNSEN, THE BOY HAS BEEN TAKEN SOUTH THROUGH THE CURSED EARTH TOWARDS TEXAS CITY.
JUDGE DREDD IS ON HIS TRAIL . . .

2000 A.D.
Credit Card:
SCRIPT ROBOT JOHN HOWARD
ART ROBOT MIKE McMAHON
LETTERING ROBOT TOM FRAME
COMPU-73E
ON YOUR RIGHT IS THE STATUE OF TEX, AND BEYOND — TEXAS CITY!
THE TALL BUILDING IS EVEREST OIL TOWER! IT'S TWO MILES HIGH AND GOT A PERMANENT SNOW CAP!
YEAH, I HEARD THEY BUILT THINGS BIG IN TEXAS CITY!

TEXAS CITY JUDGES WERE ON THE PIER –
Y'ALL HIT TOWN AT A BUSY TIME, JUDGE DREDD! THE MUTIE CLEARANCES HAVE STARTED! WE'RE SHIPPIN' 'EM ALL OUT TO NEW HOMELANDS ACROSS LAKE LOUISIANA!
TEXAS CITY WILL WALK TALL AGIN WITHOUT THEM UGLIES! Y'ALL OUGHTA KNOW – YOUR CITY DID THE SAME THING YEARS AGO!
YES. AND NOW I SEEK A MUTANT CHILD – WHO WILL ONE DAY BE CHIEF JUDGE OF MEGA-CITY ONE!
DREDD EXPLAINED HIS MISSION –
WE CAN'T SPARE YOU ANY HELP, FELLA! PA ANGEL AND HIS GANG BROKE JAIL YESTERDAY! ANY OF OUR BOYS THAT AIN'T BUSY WITH THE CLEARANCES IS OUT LOOKIN' FOR THEM.
THE ANGELS IS A BAD BUNCHA HELL-RAISERS!
I PREFER TO WORK ALONE.
DREDD WAS GIVEN ACCESS TO THE JUSTICE COMPUTER –
THE BOY HAS STRONG PRE-COG ABILITY, SO I WANT INFORMATION ON PRE-COGS WHO'VE STARTED OPERATING WITHIN THE PAST TWENTY DAYS... WHAT'S THIS? BROTHER DEATH...
...A NEW FAIRGROUND FORTUNE TELLER AT MUTIE-WORLD. HE'S BEEN UNCANNILY ACCURATE AT PREDICTING HIS CUSTOMERS' DEATHS!
IT'S GOT TO BE THE MONK! HE THINKS I'M DEAD – THAT NOBODY'S AFTER THE BOY! HE'D HAVE NO REASON TO ALTER HIS APPEARANCE!
TEXAS CITY BRED BIG MEN WHO LIKED TO LIVE DANGEROUSLY. AT DANGER PARKS LIKE MUTIEWORLD, A MAN COULD LEGALLY RISK HIS LIFE TO PROVE HIMSELF.
SOME CAME OUT WALKING TALL. MANY DIDN'T COME OUT AT ALL –
1000 lbs
STEP RIGHT UP! SHAKE HANDS WITH THE THING AND WIN A FORTUNE! ONLY 20 CREDS A TRY!
SHAKE HANDS WITH THE THING FROM THE PIT – C10000 IF YOU SURVIVE!
Y'ALL KIN DO IT, BOBBY JOE!
WALK TALL THERE, BOY!

UURGH!
OH, HARD LUCK, SIR! WHO'S NEXT FOR THE THING? DON'T ALL RUSH, FOLKS - MUTIEWORLD STAYS OPEN DESPITE THE CLEARANCES! ALL OUR MUTIES GOT PERMITS!
MUTIEWORLD'S NEWEST ATTRACTION WAS BROTHER DEATH. THE SECRET HE REVEALED HELD A SINISTER FASCINATION FOR PEOPLE -
YIPPEE! HE SAYS I'LL LIVE TO A HUNNERD AN' SIX!
FEAR
I GO AT NINETY - PEACEFULLY!

WESLEY, WHAT'S WRONG? WHAT DID HE SAY?
I...I'VE GOT THIRTY-SEVEN MINUTES! I-I'M GOING TO BE STRANGLED!
INSIDE THE BOOTH -
GREETINGS, FRIENDS! YOU COME TO LEARN THE MOMENT OF YOUR DEATH?
NO, BROTHER - WE COME TO DISCUSS YOURS!
PA ANGEL!
WHAT'RE YOU DOING HERE? YOU'RE ON THE RUN FROM THE LAW -
WE'RE LEAVIN' THE PLANET TONIGHT. BUT WE AIN'T GOIN' EMPTY-HANDED!

EARTH MONEY'S NO GOOD IN SPACE – BUT SOMEONE WHO CAN TELL THE FUTURE . . . NOW, ME AN' THE BOYS FIGURE HE'D BE VALUABLE ANYWHERE – SAVVY ?
L-LISTEN, I'M NOT REALLY THAT GOOD –
YOU AIN'T NO GOOD A-TALL, YOU TWO-CRED CONMAN! WE'RE ON TO YOUR RACKET! YOU GOT A PLUG IN YOUR EAR AN' A MUTIE KID IN BACK, TELLIN' YOU WHAT TO SAY!
HE LIED TO YOU, PA! KIN I KILL HIM NOW?
LEMME SLICE A HOLE IN HIS HEAD AN' POUR SOME POISON IN! C'MON, PA! I AIN'T DONE THAT TODAY!
THAT'S JUNIOR, MA BOY! VICIOUS LITTLE SWINE, AIN'T HE? JUST LIKE HIS PA WHEN I WAS HIS AGE!
PLEASE, PA...
YOUR HEART'S IN THE RIGHT PLACE, JUNIOR! BUT WE NEED THE MONK TO NURSEMAID THE KID. LET THE MEAN MACHINE TRY A LITTLE GENTLE PERSUASION . . .
THIS DIAL ON MY HEAD'S GOT FOUR SETTINGS, SEE! ON 1 I AIN'T VERY PLEASANT – BUT WHEN I GO UP TO 2 . . .
I GET MEAN!
AAGH!
NO!
YOU DIRTY STINKIN' RAT! YOU BE READY WITH THE KID IN ONE HOUR OR I GO UP TO 4 ON YOU!
AN' DON'T TRY TO RUN OUT, SEE! WE'LL BE AROUND, SEE – WATCHIN'!

IN THE BACK —
THE GANGSTERS HAVE BEEN, THEN...?
WHY DIDN'T YOU WARN ME ABOUT THEM, YOU LITTLE RUNT? NO GRATITUDE, THAT'S YOUR PROBLEM! AFTER ALL I'VE DONE FOR YOU!
NOBODY PUSHES ME AROUND — NOT EVEN PA ANGEL! I'LL SLIP OVER TO THE MANAGER'S OFFICE AND COLLECT MY CASH. I'LL BE OUTA HERE WITH THE KID BEFORE THEY KNOW IT!
IT WAS BROTHER DEATH'S MISFORTUNE TO MEET JUDGE DREDD ARRIVING —
MUTIE WORLD
YOU! MONK!
IT'S THAT BLASTED JUDGE! HE OUGHTA BE DEAD!
WE'LL STAY BY YOU, WESLEY! NO WAY ARE YOU GONNA GET STRANGLED!
OUTA THE WAY!
WESLEY!
UNNNGH!
AGH!
SKRUNCH!

That's it for The Judge Child in this book. Pick up the story in Rebellion's *The Complete Case Files 04*.

JUDGE DREDD

IN

OTTO SUMP'S UGLY CLINIC

JUDGE

2000 A.D.
Credit Card:
SCRIPT ROBOT T. B. GROVER
ART ROBOT RON SMITH
LETTERING ROBOT TOM FRAME
COMPU·73E

MEET OTTO SUMP

HEY, YOU!

WHO, ME?

THAT'S RIGHT, PAL — YOU! MISTER NOBODY!
WHADDYA MEAN, "MISTER NOBODY"?
THAT'S WHAT YOU ARE, PAL! LOOK AROUND YOU!
THERE ARE EIGHT HUNDRED MILLION OTHERS IN THIS CITY — EVERY ONE OF THEM JUST LIKE YOU! DULL — BORING — ORDINARY! INSTANTLY FORGETTABLE!
HAVEN'T YOU EVER WANTED TO STAND OUT FROM THE CROWD? HAVEN'T YOU EVER WANTED TO GET UP AND SHOUT — LOOK AT ME! I'M SOMEBODY!
I SURE HAVE! B-BUT HOW — ?
I'LL TELL YOU HOW, PA
GET UGLY!

MEET OTTO SUMP

MY **UGLY CLINICS** ARE OPEN ALL OVER THE CITY. BELIEVE ME, ONE VISIT AND NO-ONE WILL EVER FORGET YOU AGAIN! **OTTO SUMP GUARANTEES IT!**

BE THE TALK OF YOUR BLOCK WITH AN UGLY

OTTO SUMP'S UGLY CLINIC

O SUMP HAD FIRST HIT THE HEADLINES AFTER HIS APPEARANCE ON "**SOB STORY**", THE VIDPROG WHERE GUESTS BEGGED FOR MONEY. *

DON'T TELL ME ABOUT UGLY! I GOT UGLY COMIN' OUTA MY **EARS**!

SOB STORY

MTV

* SEE PROG 132

OTTO'S "UGLY" ROUTINE HAD MADE HIM THE BIGGEST MONEY-EARNER IN THE PROGRAMME'S HISTORY –

VIEWERS HAVE SENT YOU OVER **SIXTY-MILLION CREDS**, MR SUMP! WHAT DO YOU INTEND TO DO WITH YOUR FORTUNE?

UH... I'M GONNA INVEST IT!

I'M GONNA BUY ME A WHOLE CHAIN OF **BEAUTY CLINICS**, SO THAT NOBODY NEVER HAS TO BE AS UGLY AS ME AGAIN!

OTTO SUMP'S BEAUTY CLINIC

AAAAAAAAAHH!

IN OTTO'S LESS-THAN-SKILFUL HANDS, **DISASTER** WAS ONLY TO BE EXPECTED –

MY HAIR! MY FACE! WH-WHAT HAVE YOU **DONE** TO ME?
UH... I AIN'T QUITE SURE, LADY!
MISTER SUMP!
OTTO

I KNOW I ASKED FOR A FACE LIFT, BUT THIS IS **RIDICULOUS**!

I'M NEVER COMING BACK HERE AGAIN! **NEVER**!
MR SUMP **WILL** INSIST ON TREATING THE CLIENTS HIMSELF! HE'S **RUINING** US!

THEN ONE DAY A WOMAN ASKED TO SPEAK TO OTTO IN PRIVATE –
I BELIEVE YOU TREATED A FRIEND OF MINE – TABITHA SPARKS WAS HER NAME.
UH, YEAH, THAT WAS THE FACE BURNS AND THE BROKEN TEETH – BUT I CAN EXPLAIN, LADY –
I DON'T WANT TO KNOW HOW YOU DID IT, MR SUMP – I JUST WANT YOU TO DO THE SAME TO ME!
UHHH...?
I WAS AT A PARTY LAST NIGHT AND TABITHA SPARKS WAS THE CENTRE OF ATTRACTION! SHE'S ALWAYS FIRST WITH THE NEW FASHIONS, OF COURSE... BUT UGLINESS! ONLY SHE COULD THINK OF IT! THE REST OF US WERE QUITE GREEN WITH ENVY!
YOU'VE GOT TO HELP ME, MR SUMP! I WANT TO BE EVEN UGLIER THAN TABITHA!
TABITHA SPARKS WAS THE CITY'S ACKNOWLEDGED FASHION QUEEN. AS MORE FOLLOWED HER LEAD, SOMETHING CLICKED IN OTTO'S DULL BRAIN –
MY DEAR! YOU LOOK SO WONDERFULLY... DIFFERENT!
THANK YOU, DEAR! I LOVE YOUR "UGLY" TOO!
I'VE HIT ON SOMETHING HERE!
PAY DESK
AND SO AN EMPIRE WAS BORN. THE CRAZE SWEPT LIKE WILDFIRE AMONG THE CITY'S BORED MASSES –
SUDDENLY, UGLINESS WAS IN!
SUMP TOWER
WE NEED OTTO
OTTO SUMP'S UGLY CLINIC
OPEN
GET UGLY
SUMP

SOON, A WHOLE RANGE OF OTTO SUMP UGLY PRODUCTS APPEARED IN THE SHOPS –
THE BEAUTY COUNTER
402
HEY! THEY'VE GOT PIMPLEX! THAT GIVES YOU SOME GREAT ZITS!
I WANT TO BE NOTICED! HAVE YOU GOT ANY OF THAT STUFF THAT GIVES YOU STALE BREATH AND TOOTH DECAY?
SUMP PASTE? YES INDEED, MADAM!
THE UGLY COUNTER
SUMP
BULGING
OTTO SUMP PRODUCTS
FLABBON FOR USE AS PART OF YOUR UNCONTROLLED DIET
SUMP PASTE FOR STALE BREATH AND TOOTH DECAY
SCUM ROLL-ON-ODORANT
PIMPLEX FOR PIMPLES ZITS AND ACNE.
MIXED BOILS FOR PAINFUL AND UNSIGHTLY SORES
SCAB POWDER
WART-ON WART INDUCER
LIP CHAPPER
BLEMISH CREAM
DANDRUFF SHAMPOO MEDICATED AGAINST MEDICATION
OTTO'S MILLIONS WERE PLOUGHED INTO A HIGH-POWERED ADVERTISING CAMPAIGN –
HE'S NOT!
HE IS!
HE'S NOT!
HE IS!
HE IS!
GAAAH!
HE'S USING OTTO SUMP'S DANDRUFF SHAMPOO!
SUMP DANDRUFF SHAMPOO MEDICATED AGAINST MEDICATION
JUST ONE OF A RANGE OF OTTO SUMP UGLY PRODUCTS!
THE CRAZE CAUGHT ON QUICKLY AMONG THE YOUNG. NOW GANGS OF YOUTHS KNOWN AS "PUGLIES" ROAMED THE STREETS, CAUSING TROUBLE –
SHUGGY HALL
OUT MY WAY!
Y-SUMP OKAY, DULLO!
BUT NOT EVERYONE LOVED OTTO –
YOU UGLIES ARE COMING TO THE WRONG PLACE!

OTTO SUMP IS CLOSING DOWN!
AAAAA!
BBBADOOMM!
JUDGE DREDD WAS FIRST ON THE SCENE –
SOMEBODY'S DISCOVERED A NEW TREATMENT, GET AMBULANCES DOWN TO THE SUMP CLINIC ON PARADI E AND 4TH!
DO THE USUAL FORENSIC TESTS. I'M GOING TO QUESTION THE OWNER OF THE CLINIC.
RIGHT, DREDD.
DREDD
SCUM
ROLL-ON-ODORANT
THE 18-HOUR PONG
SCUM'S THE WORD!
ATTENTION, JUDGE DREDD! WE HAVE ANOTHER BOMB ATTACK – SUMP CLINIC, 2088TH STREET!
KEEP ME INFORMED. I'LL HANDLE THIS ONE MYSELF!
SUMP TOWER
LOOKS LIKE SOMEONE'S TRYING TO PUT OTTO SUMP OUT OF BUSINESS – AND THEY'RE USING PRETTY UGLY METHODS!
NEXT PROG:
GHASTLY INC.!

JUDGE DREDD

ADVERTISEMENT

9 STEPS TO UGLY

HEY THERE! TIRED OF BEING HANDSOME? WHY NOT STAND OUT FROM THE CROWD WITH OTTO SUMP'S UGLY PRODUCTS! HERE ARE 9 SIMPLE STEPS TO HELP YOU TO PERFECT UGLINESS!

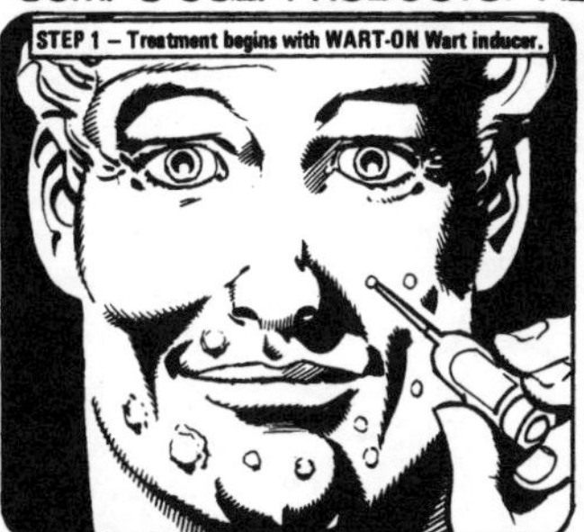

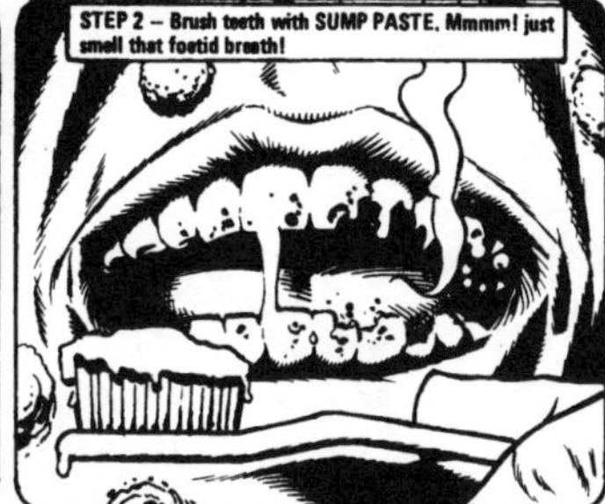

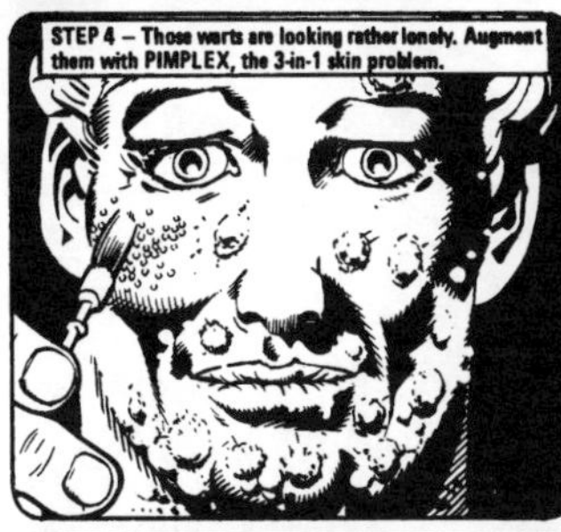

GET WISE! GET UGLY! GET OTTO SUMP!

For a full range of Otto Sump Ugly Products, send SAE to SUMP TOWER, District 12.

OTTO SUMP'S UGLY CLINIC PART 2.
THE LATEST FAD TO HIT MEGA-CITY ONE HAD MUSHROOMED OVERNIGHT INTO A MULTI-MILLION CREDIT BUSINESS. BEHIND THE UGLY CRAZE WAS A MILLIONAIRE TYCOON AND FORMER SOB STORY CONTESTANT OTTO SUMP —
2000 A.D. Credit Card
SCRIPT ROBOT T.B. GROVER
ART ROBOT RON SMITH
LETTERING ROBOT TOM FRAME
9 STEPS TO UGLY
OKAY, THAT AD LOOKS GREAT! RUN IT IN EVERY VID-MAG IN TOWN!
JUDGE DREDD TO SEE YOU, MR SUMP!
JUDGE DREDD! THIS IS AN HONOUR! I KNEW YOU'D COME TO VISIT YOUR OLD PAL SOONER OR LATER!
STOP HUGGING ME, CITIZEN SUMP! OUR FORMER ACQUAINTANCE GIVES YOU NO RIGHT TO FAMILIARITY!
DIDN'T MEAN NO HARM, JUDGE! LAST THING I WANT TO DO IS OFFEND THE FOUNDER OF MY UGLY EMPIRE!
WHAAAT?
JUDGE DREDD
SOB STORY
OUR FOUNDER
OTTO SUMP
SURE THING! IF YOU HADN'T GOT ME ON SOB STORY, I'D NEVER HAVE GOT STARTED! I WAS EVEN THINKIN' OF PUTTING "BY APPOINTMENT TO JUDGE DREDD" ON MY PRODUCTS!

USING THE IMAGE OF A JUDGE IN A COMMERCIAL VENTURE IS ILLEGAL, CITIZEN! YOU'VE HAD ONE WARNING – YOU WON'T GET ANOTHER!
AW, GEE!

NOW PERHAPS WE CAN GET TO WHY I'M HERE. ARE YOU AWARE, CITIZEN, THAT TWO OF YOUR UGLY CLINICS HAVE BEEN BOMBED?
UH, YEAH, I DID HEAR SOMETHING...
AND YOU'RE NOT WORRIED?
NAW! I GOT FAITH IN THE JUDGES, JUDGE!

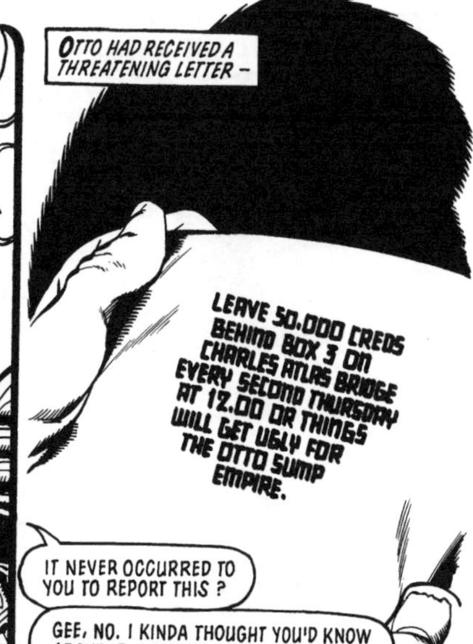
OTTO HAD RECEIVED A THREATENING LETTER –
LEAVE 50,000 CREDS BEHIND BOX 3 ON CHARLES ATLAS BRIDGE EVERY SECOND THURSDAY AT 12.00 OR THINGS WILL GET UGLY FOR THE OTTO SUMP EMPIRE.
IT NEVER OCCURRED TO YOU TO REPORT THIS?
GEE, NO. I KINDA THOUGHT YOU'D KNOW ABOUT IT. I MEAN, YOU JUDGES KNOW EVERYTHING, DON'T YOU?

WHHUMMP!

I KNOW WHAT THAT IS ANYWAY! EXPLOSION!
LIFT
SUMP TOWER RECEPTION WAS A SLAUGHTERHOUSE –
TWO MEN – WITH BLACK HOODS! THEY RAN OUT!

BLOOD! THEY MUST HAVE BEEN CAUGHT IN THE BLAST!

WE'RE THERE, MERC!

WHOOOHOO

TOO LATE! A JUDGE!

DRIVE — AAAGH!

BLAM-BLAM

FIZZZZ.ZZZ

ADVERTISEMENT

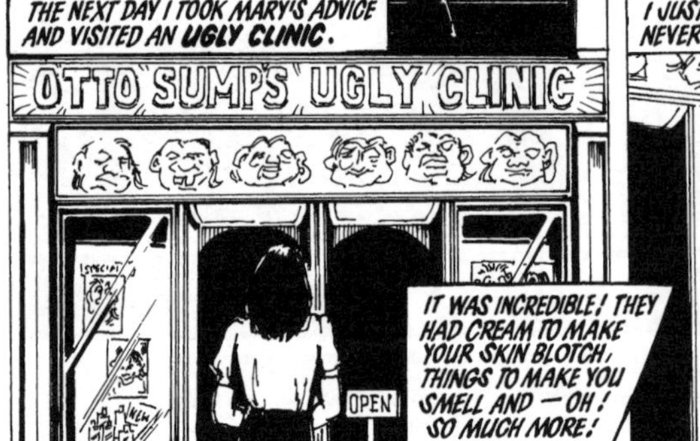

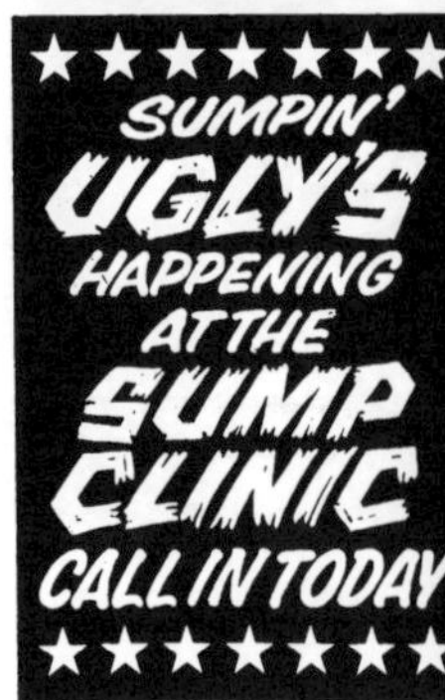

THEY'RE CUTTING CROSS TRAFFIC! GONNA BE A PILE-UP –
DREDD'S BIKE CANNON PREVENTS A DISASTROUS ACCIDENT –
RROARRR-RRR....
– BY EFFICIENTLY REMOVING THE DANGER!
BOOOM!
THEY'RE NOT GOING TO BE DOING MUCH TALKING. PITY! COULD HAVE USED A FEW WORDS.
MERC RAMSAY AND SPIDER SCHULTZ – TWO CHEAP HOODS WORKING FOR THE MANTIS SYNDICATE. SO THE MANTIS BROTHERS ARE BEHIND THESE PROTECTION DEMANDS.
BUT THERE'S NO WAY OF PROVING IT UNLESS... DEAD MEN TALK.
THAT NIGHT –
TWO MEN APPREHENDED AFTER THE BOMBING OF SUMP TOWER ARE NOW BEING TREATED IN THE INTENSIVE CARE UNIT OF THE MARCUS WELBY GENERAL HOSPITAL. WHEN THE MEN ARE WELL ENOUGH TO TALK, JUDGES EXPECT FURTHER ARRESTS.
THE MANTIS BROTHERS –
MERC AND SPIDER WOULD NEVER TALK!
DON'T BE SO SURE! JUDGES CAN MAKE MEN DO ANYTHING!
RACE NEWS

THEN WE'RE GOING TO HAVE TO SHUT THEM UP FOR GOOD!
LATER, AN AMBULANCE SCREAMS TO A STOP OUTSIDE MARCUS WELBY CASUALTY.
INTENSIVE CARE UNIT — QUICKLY! WE'VE GOT A CROAKER!
THAT WAY!

INTENSIVE CARE UNIT

RAMSAY
SCHULTZ
NO UNAUTHORISED PERSONNEL
NOBODY ON GUARD! THIS IS ALMOST TOO GOOD TO BE TRUE!

SORRY, BOYS, I HATE TO HAVE TO WIPE YOU OUT, BUT —
D.O.A
HELL! DEAD ON ARRIVAL!

THEY SAY DEAD MEN DON'T TALK, BUT THOSE TWO SAID PLENTY. YOU'RE UNDER ARREST.
DREDD!

CON MANTIS SEALED HIS FATE —
YOU'LL NEVER TAKE — AAAGH!
THE DYING MAN'S BULLETS RIPPED THROUGH THE DOOR — AND INTO A PASSING ROBOSURGEON —
RATTA-TAT-TAT!

OPERATE! OPERATE! I MUST OPERATE!
DROKK! ROBODOC ON THE RAMPAGE!
CRASH!
NEXT PROG: OTTO'S EMPIRE STRIKES BACK!

JUDGE DREDD
JUDGE
OTTO SUMP'S UGLY CLINIC PART 3.
THE MANTIS BROTHERS' PROTECTION SYNDICATE HAD BEEN BOMBING OTTO SUMP'S UGLY CLINICS. NOW DREDD HAS TRAPPED THEM IN THE MARCUS WELBY INTENSIVE CARE UNIT — BUT A DAMAGED ROBO-SURGEON IS ON THE RAMPAGE —
2000 A.D. Credit Card
SCRIPT ROBOT T.B. GROVER
ART ROBOT RON SMITH
LETTERING ROBOT TOM FRAME
COMPU-73E
OPERATE! OPERATE! I MUST OPERATE!
DREDD
IT'S CUTTING ME!

THE ROBOT'S GONE HAYWIRE!
LOTS OF LOVELY BONE AND GRISTLE! GOT TO COME OUT! EVERY BIT OF IT!
HELP ME!
DREDD

FIZZZZZZZ
ZAT!

CARE UNIT
ABE MANTIS SEIZED HIS CHANCE TO MAKE A RUN FOR IT –
CITIZENS IN THE WAY! CAN'T SHOOT!

BIM MANTIS WAS STILL ALIVE –
DREDD'S GONE... GOT TO GET OUT...
SNIK!
WHAT THE...?
OPE...RATE! OPE...RATE! STILL TIME TO OPE...RATE!
NO! IT CAN'T BE!

OUT IT COMES! AND THAT! AND THAT! AND THAT –
AIEEEEEEEE!

MEANWHILE –
WHUMP
OUT OF THE WAY!

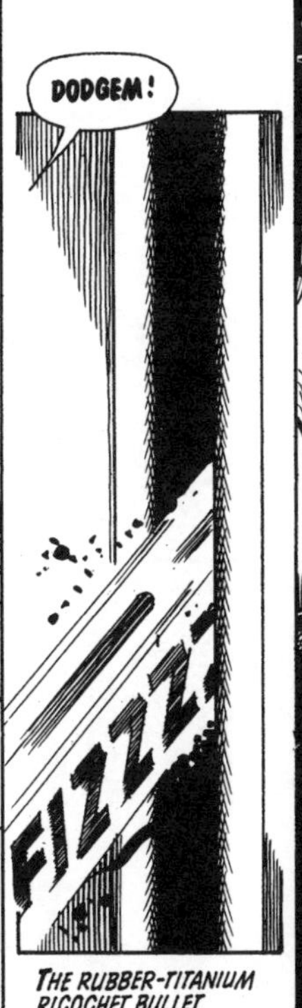

THE RUBBER-TITANIUM RICOCHET BULLET ALWAYS GETS ITS MAN!

THE UGLY CLINIC BOMBINGS WERE OVER, BUT FOR DREDD THE CASE WAS NOT YET CLOSED. NEXT MORNING HE CALLED ON OTTO SUMP, CREATOR OF THE UGLY CRAZE –
YOU'RE A PAL, JUDGE DREDD! I KNEW YOU WOULDN'T LET THOSE HOODLUMS CLOSE MY BUSINESS DOWN!
I DID MY JOB, NOTHING MORE. IN MY OPINION, THE MANTIS BROTHERS HAD THE RIGHT IDEA – THEY JUST USED THE WRONG METHODS!

YOUR CLINICS ARE UGLY, SUMP! A POSITIVE DANGER TO THE HEALTH OF THE COMMUNITY! I'M TELLING YOU THAT I WANT THEM CLOSED – TODAY!
GEE, JUDGE, THERE'S NOTHING ILLEGAL ABOUT MY CLINICS...
DREDD

VERY WELL – IF YOU WON'T CLOSE THEM, I WILL! AND I'LL DO IT LEGALLY!
DREDD

THAT DAY DREDD BEGAN HIS CAMPAIGN AGAINST OTTO SUMP'S UGLY EMPIRE. UNDER HIS DIRECTIONS, JUSTICE DEPARTMENT STANDARDS OFFICERS INVESTIGATED SUMP ADVERTISING AND PRODUCTS –

OTTO SUMP'S WINDY
FOR THE PERFECT BELCH!
FALSE CLAIM – NOTHING'S PERFECT! THAT AD IS BANNED!

THEY LOOK LIKE VERUCCAS, BUT THEY'RE ONLY SWOLLEN SKIN. IMPOUND ALL STOCKS OF SUMP'S VERRUCA PASTE!
VERUCCA PASTE
OTTO SUMP

DREDD LED CRIME BLITZES ON OTTO'S UGLY CLINICS –
EVERYBODY AGAINST THE WALL! SEARCH THEM!
OTTO SUMP CLINIC
UGLY

EVERY CITIZEN HAD SOMETHING TO HIDE. WHEN NECESSARY, THE JUDGES COULD ALWAYS FIND IT –
TAKE THEM AWAY!
BLACK MARIA
DREDD

JUDGE DREDD'S VICIOUS CAMPAIGN AGAINST OTTO SUMP'S HARMLESS UGLY CLINICS CONTINUES UNABATED! THIS PROGRAMME DEMANDS TO KNOW WHEN THIS PERSECUTION OF AN INNOCENT CITIZEN WILL STOP!
AND NOW, A WORD FROM OUR SPONSOR –

THE FIRST DATE IS ALWAYS DIFFICULT. WHY NOT IMPRESS HER WITH OTTO SUMP'S NEW DEAD SKUNK AFTERSHAVE?
SHE'LL REMEMBER YOU FOREVER!

ON THE THIRD DAY, A MASSED GROUP OF UGLIES MARCHED IN PROTEST THROUGH THE CITY STREETS —
HANDS OFF OTTO SUMP
UGLY IS BEAUTIFUL
SUMP O.K.
ILLEGAL MARCH! GET ME WEATHER CONTROL!

WEATHER CONTROL COULD PROGRAMME RAIN WITH STREET-BY-STREET ACCURACY —

THAT'LL DAMPEN THEIR ENTHUSIASM!

THIS WHOLE BUSINESS IS GETTING OUT OF HAND. IT'S TIME I STOPPED BEING SO **SOFT** ON THEM!

THERE WAS STILL ONE COURSE OF ACTION LEFT OPEN — THE OLDEST TRICK IN THE BOOK. NEXT DAY, THE FIRST **UGLY TAX** WAS IMPOSED —

OTTO SUMP PRODUCTS

1000 C TAX

BLOBTREX, SIR? CERTAINLY! THAT WILL BE 49 CREDS — PLUS 1,000 CREDS **UGLY TAX**.

ONE THOUSAND CREDS? IT'S **OUTRAGEOUS**!

THERE'S 1,000 CREDS TAX ON ALL UGLY PRODUCTS!

1000 CREDS FOR ALL UGLY PRODS

BUT **NOBODY** CAN AFFORD TO PAY THAT!

UGLY CLINIC

CLOSED OWING TO UGLY TAX

THE UGLY CRAZE DIED AS QUICKLY AS IT HAD BEEN BORN —

BUT ONE UGLY CLINIC DID MANAGE TO REMAIN OPEN —

WELCOME, MADAM. PLEASE STEP INSIDE. MONSIEUR LE SUMP, 'E WILL ATTEND TO YOU IN LE MOMENT!

OF COURSE, OTTO FOUND HIS NEW FRENCH ACCENT DIFFICULT TO MASTER. BUT HIS CLIENTS EXPECTED IT, AND THEY WERE USED TO GETTING THEIR OWN WAY...

OTTO LE SUMP HIGH CLASS UGLIFIER

UGLINESS TO THE FEELTHY RICH

FOR NOW, ONLY THE RICH COULD AFFORD TO BE UGLY!

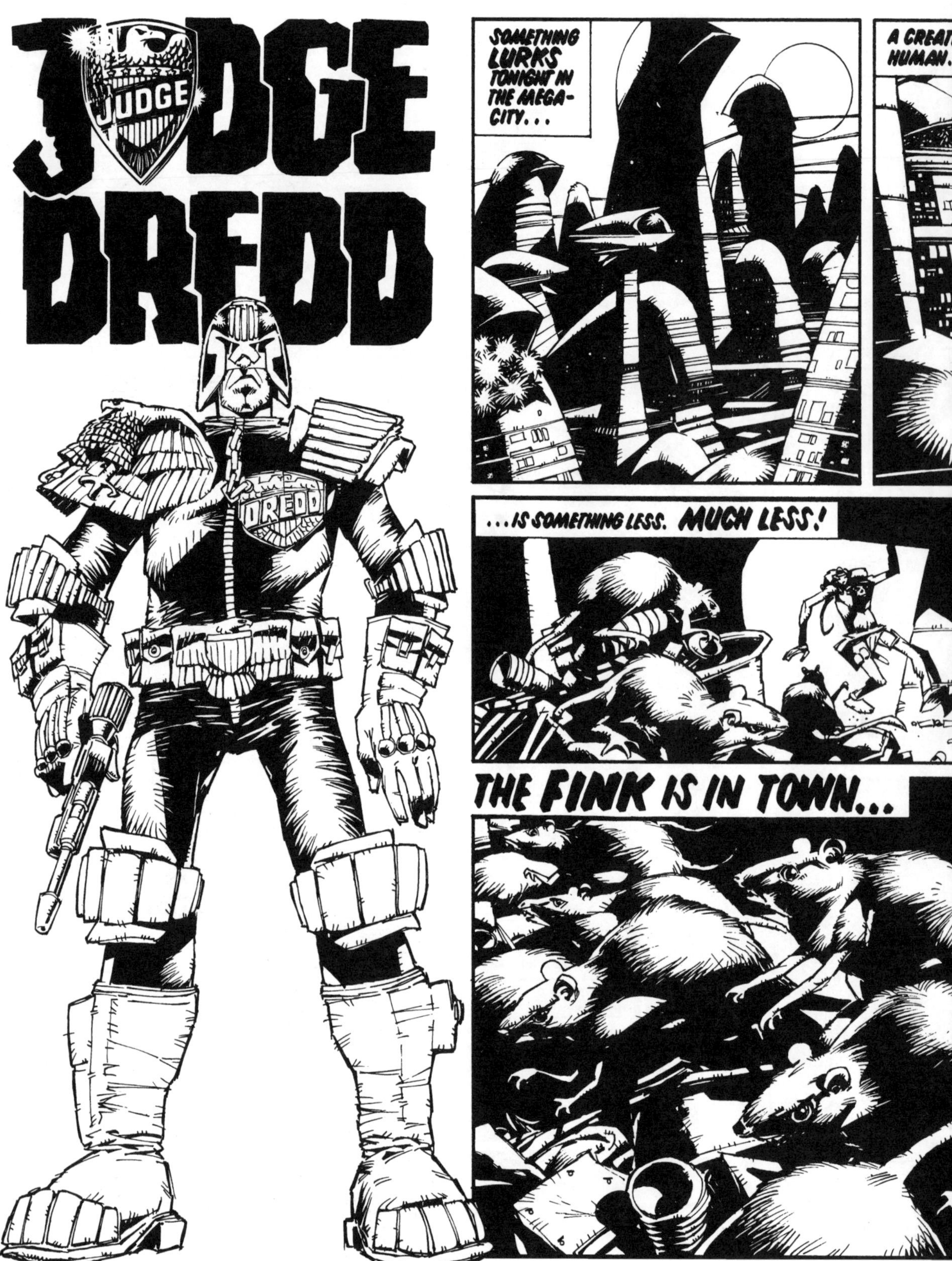
JUDGE DREDD
JUDGE
DREDD
SOMETHING LURKS TONIGHT IN THE MEGA-CITY...
A CREAT
HUMAN.
...IS SOMETHING LESS. MUCH LESS!
THE FINK IS IN TOWN...

HE HAS COME TO KILL!
THE FINK
2000 A.D. Credit Card:
SCRIPT ROBOT T. B. GROVER
ART ROBOT MIKE McMAHON
LETTERING ROBOT TOM FRAME
COMPU-73E
McMAHON

AT MEGA-CITY SPACEPORT, JUDGE PILOT LARTER BEDS DOWN JUSTICE! . . .
WE'VE GOT THAT LUNA FLIGHT TOMORROW. HAVE HER READY AT 0700.
YES, SIR.

LARTER TO CONTROL! SIGNING OFF FOR THE NIGHT. ANY MESSAGES FOR ME?

IN AN ALLEY, PINK EYES GLINT –
HERE COMES THAT THAR, JUDGE, RATTY...
TIME TO PIZEN UP!

NO MESSAGES, LARTER. SLEEP WELL.
I WILL.

SHHUNK!

STOMM! I'VE BEEN HIT!

MUSCLES... SEIZING UP! CAN'T MOVE!

BY THE TIME LARTER STRIKES THE GROUND, HE IS STIFF AS A BOARD –
WE GOTTIM, RATTY! PIZENED HIM GOOD!

THAT THAR WAS MY BEST PARALYZIN' PIZEN! YOU AWAKE IN THERE, JUDGE?
SURE YOU ARE! CAN'T MOVE A MUSCLE, BUT YOU KIN SEE AN' FEEL EVERYTHIN' THAT'S GONNA HAPPEN TO YOU...

WE GOT A REAL CUTE LITTLE SURPRISE COOKED UP FOR HIM, AIN'T WE, RATTY BOY?

AND LARTER CAN ONLY STARE...

...AND WONDER!

A PATROLLING JUDGE FOUND LARTER'S BIKE TEN MINUTES LATER –
IT'S CRASHED! NO SIGN OF LARTER!
WE'LL PUT OUT A CALL FOR HIM!

CONTROL TO LARTER! REPORT YOUR POSITION! REPEAT – REPORT YOUR POSITION!
LISTEN, RATTY! THEY'RE CALLIN' HIM!

BUT THIS HERE JUDGE HAS MADE HIS LAST REPORT!
THIS CREEP'S NOT HUMAN! THERE'S SOMETHING ABOUT THAT TWISTED FACE... SOMETHING FAMILIAR!

WHAT'S THAT, RATTY? YOU WANT TO GIT STARTED? OKAY, AIN'T NO SENSE DELAYIN'! CALL YOUR PALS!

ALL THROUGH THE SEWER, RATS RESPONDED TO THE CALL—

DROKK! NO!

THEY **AIN'T** SO TOUGH AS YOU CURSED EARTH RATS, RATTY! BUT THAT'S ALL FER THE GOOD. THEY'LL MAKE A NICE **SLOW** JOB OF HIM...

AND A TEAR APPEARS IN THE CRAZY PINK EYES –
IT'S THE WAY PA WOULD'VE WANTED IT !

THEY FIND LARTER AN HOUR LATER... WHAT'S LEFT OF HIM!
BACK, YOU DEVILS!

THE MURDERER MUST HAVE DRAGGED HIM DOWN HERE. WHOEVER HE WAS, HE'S LEFT A CALLING CARD...

FINK
STRANGE. LOOKS LIKE... AN ANGEL!

AND IN A BACKSTREET DEMOLITION SITE –
ONE DOWN, RATTY BOY...
DANGER
DEMOLITION
KEEP OUT

TWO TO GO!
DREDD
NEXT PROG: FINK IN THE DRINK!

IN THE SHADOWS OF A MEGA-CITY ALLEY, A STRANGE HALF-HUMAN CREATURE LURKS –

HE IS THE FINK. HE HAS KILLED ONCE ALREADY –

BUT ONCE IS NOT ENOUGH!

M-MY LIFE!
DEAD!
HERE COMES A JUDGE! THANK THE LAW!

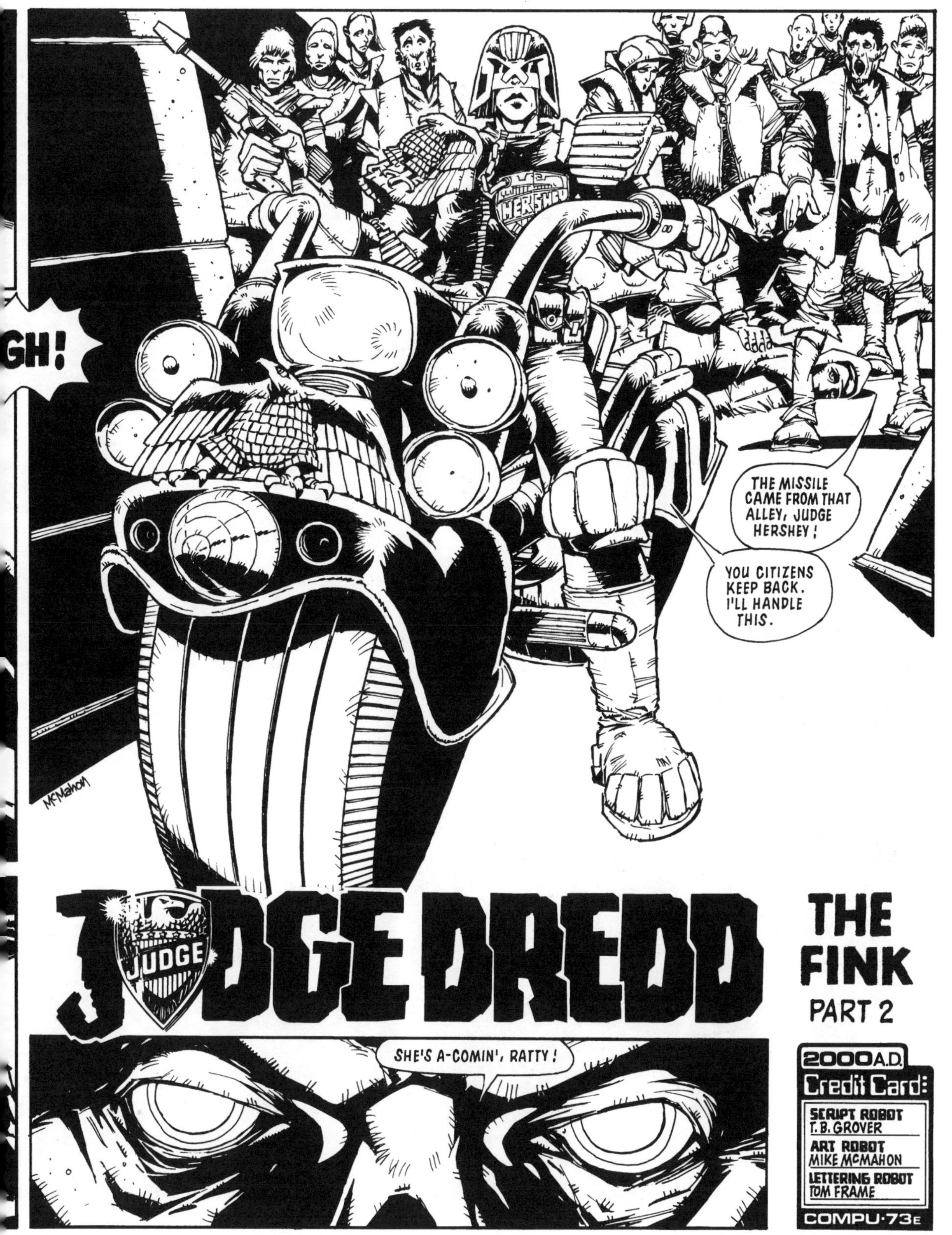

GH!
THE MISSILE CAME FROM THAT ALLEY, JUDGE HERSHEY!
YOU CITIZENS KEEP BACK. I'LL HANDLE THIS.
McMahon
JUDGE DREDD
THE FINK
PART 2
SHE'S A-COMIN', RATTY!
2000 A.D. Credit Card:
SCRIPT ROBOT T.B. GROVER
ART ROBOT MIKE McMAHON
LETTERING ROBOT TOM FRAME
COMPU-73E

MEANWHILE, ACROSS CITY, JUDGE LARTER'S REMAINS ARE BEING BROUGHT FROM THE SEWER –
WE THOUGHT YOU'D BE INTERESTED, JUDGE DREDD. LARTER WAS YOUR PILOT ON THE JUDGE CHILD MISSION.
SO IT WAS MURDER!
RATS KILLED HIM... BUT FORENSIC SAY HIS SYSTEM CONTAINED A STRONG PARALYSING POISON.

SEEMS THE KILLER LEFT HIS SIGNATURE...
AN ANGEL...?
FINK
DIDN'T YOU HAVE A RUN IN WITH THE ANGEL GANG ON XANADU*? MAYBE THEY'VE COME LOOKING FOR REVENGE...
THE ANGEL GANG ARE DEAD. CAN'T BE THEM. UNLESS... DROKK!
* SEE PROGS 177-181–THARG.

I WANT AN OPEN LINE TO JUDGE HERSHEY! THIS IS PRIORITY ONE!

HERSHEY! THIS IS DREDD! ARE YOU READING ME?
LOUD AND CLEAR. GO AHEAD.

LARTER IS DEAD. YOU MAY BE THE KILLER'S NEXT TARGET!
I BELIEVE THERE MAY BE A FIFTH ANGEL! REPEAT –

–A FIFTH ANGEL!

SHE'S BEEN CUT OFF! CONTROL! GIVE ME A FIX ON HERSHEY!
DOGGONE! THESE... MEGA-CITY JUDGE WUMMEN... IS TOUGH!
THAT'S RIGHT, CREEP —
THIS TOUGH!
NNNG!
GOING FER HER GUN... GIT HER, RATTY!
DROKK!
UUHHHHH...

CONTROL TO DREDD. JUDGE HERSHEY LAST REPORTED IN PURSUIT OF **UNKNOWN PERP** IN **LAST CHANCE LANE!**
ON OUR WAY!

MY **PARALYZIN' PIZEN'S** KNOCKED THE KICK OUT OUT O'HER, RATTY! LET'S GIT HER IN THE BAG!

HALT!
JUDGES!

HOTEL Oddfellow
HOTEL ODDFELLOW STAFF ONLY
IN THIS HERE HOTEL, RATTY!

TABLE FOR ONE, SIR? **ZZZZ**ZZZTrr!
GOOD LORD! WHAT IS **THAT**?

POOL
THEM THAR JUDGES'LL BE AFTER US, RATTY! GOTTA SLOW 'EM UP —
MY HEAVY DUTY PIZENIN' PIZEN!

THE POISON ACTS QUICKLY —
I'M BURNING UP!
HELP ME!
MEDI-SQUADS TO THE HOTEL ODDFELLOW! WE'VE GOT A **MASS POISONING!**

THE EXIT FROM THE POOL LEADS STRAIGHT ONTO THE STREET.
DROKK IT!

LOOKS LIKE WE'VE LOST HIM, DREDD!

BUT IN THE TRAFFIC –
HUH? INSTRUMENTS SHOW I'VE PICKED UP A PASSENGER!

MY STARS! IT – IT'S NOT HUMAN!
SLEEPYBYE
SUCTION BEDS

DANG! SEEN US!

FIX HIM, RATTY BOY!

HELLO, SLEEPYBYE CONTROL! THIS IS FRANK IN TRUCK 7! COME IN, PLEASE!

SLEEPYBYE CONTROL TO TRUCK 7. WHAT'S YOUR PROBLEM, FRANK ?

HELLO...? FRANK...?

THE BITE OF THE CURSED EARTH RAT IS FATAL !
KRAASH
LOOK OUT !

STILL NO FIX ON HERSHEY, DREDD. BUT RECORDS HAVE COME UP WITH SOMETHING INTERESTING...THERE IS A FIFTH ANGEL !
FINK ANGEL, ELDEST SON OF ELMER "PA" ANGEL. A RIGHT POISONOUS LITTLE CHARACTER HE IS !

HERSHEY WAS ON THE JUDGE CHILD MISSION, TOO. YOU THINK THIS FINK HEARD ABOUT HIS FAMILY AND CAME LOOKING FOR REVENGE ?
I KNOW IT !

UNLESS WE FIND HERSHEY, SHE'S GOING TO KNOW IT TOO !
NEXT PROG:
THE MAKING OF A FINK !

PROG 527
20 JUNE 87
2000 AD
FEATURING JUDGE DREDD
$1.70 Malaysia
75c Australia
85c New Zealand
(Inc. G.S.T.)
88g Mercury
210g Venus
66g Mars
110g Saturn
2g Pluto
429g Neptune
28p
EARTH MONEY
IN ORBIT EVERY MONDAY
DREDD
BETTER DREDD THAN DEAD!

IN A HOLE BENEATH A MEGA-CITY DEMOLITION SITE, A STRANGE HALF-HUMAN CREATURE SITS. HIS NAME IS **THE FINK**. HE IS A KILLER.

BESIDE HIM HANGS JUDGE HERSHEY. A POWERFUL PARALYSING POISON COURSES THROUGH HER. SHE CANNOT MOVE, CANNOT SPEAK, ONLY THINK . . .

. . . AND **WONDER** . . . !
SO HE'S THE **FIFTH ANGEL** — COME TO AVENGE THE EXECUTION OF HIS FAMILY!
IF HE'S GOING TO KILL ME, WHY DOESN'T HE DO IT? WHAT IS HE **WAITING** FOR . . . ?

THE FINK IS WAITING FOR NIGHT, FOR DARKNESS TO CLOAK HIS NEXT MURDEROUS ACT . . .
MEANWHILE HE WAITS . . . AND REMEMBERS. BACK TO THE TIMES THAT USED TO BE . . .
. . . THE TIMES THAT WOULD NEVER COME AGAIN!
IT ALL BEGAN IN A MEAN CURSED EARTH SHACK NOT FAR FROM TEXAS CITY . . .
IT'S A BOY!
MA'S A GONER, I'M AFRAID, BOYS — BUT AFORE SHE WENT SHE GAVE US A REAL VICIOUS LITTLE TYKE! LOOKIT HIM — BITIN' NEAR CLEAN THROUGH TO THE BONE!
2000 A.D.
Credit Card
SCRIPT ROBOT T.B. GROVER
ART ROBOT MIKE McMAHON
LETTERING ROBOT TOM FRAME
COMPU-73E
THE FINK PART THREE

DON'T Y'ALL WORRY, MA. I'LL BRING YOUR BOYS UP RIGHT. I'LL MAKE 'EM THE MOST VICIOUS, ORNERIEST, BADDEST FAMILY THE WORLD'S EVER SEEN! DANG TOOTIN' I WILL!
MA ANGEL GONE TO HELL
MA ANGEL WOULD HAVE BEEN PROUD OF THE WAY PA SET ABOUT HIS TASK...
BEIN' BAD IS EASY, BOYS – BUT BEIN' SUPERBAD REQUIRES YEARS O' PRACTICE!
EACH O' YOU HAS GOTTA CULTY-VATE AN INDIVIDUAL STYLE – THAT WAYS YOUR VICTIMS REMEMBERS YOU... ALL THE WAY TO THE GRAVE!
LINK AND JUNIOR TOOK TO THEIR TRAINING LIKE 'SKEETERS TO FRESH BLOOD...
LET ME LOOSE, PA! I FEEL THE URGE TO KILL A-COMIN' ON!
GOO GOO!
FINK ANGEL, PA'S ELDEST, WAS ALREADY A STYLIST. A BORN LONER, AT THE AGE OF 7 HE HAD GONE TO LIVE IN A HOLE...
I AIN'T A-COMIN' OUT, PA! DON'T Y'ALL TRY TO MAKE ME OR I'LL HAVE TO KILL YA!
THAT'S MA BOY!
THE ONLY FLY IN PA'S OINTMENT WAS YOUNG "MEAN" ANGEL...
SOMETHING'S GONNA HAFTA BE DONE ABOUT THAT THAR BOY!
STYLE = FEAR
AND SO, NOT LONG AFTERWARDS, THE ANGEL GANG MADE THEIR FIRST RAID ON TEXAS CITY...
C. FASSBINDER BIOMETRIC SURG
NEXT!
RECKON THAT'S US, BOYS! THESE KIND FOLK SEEM TO HAVE DIED ON US – JUS' WHEN WE WAS GETTIN' ACQUAINTED, TOO!
YOU'RE A-COMIN' WITH US, DOC!
ULP! WH-WHATEVER YOU SAY!

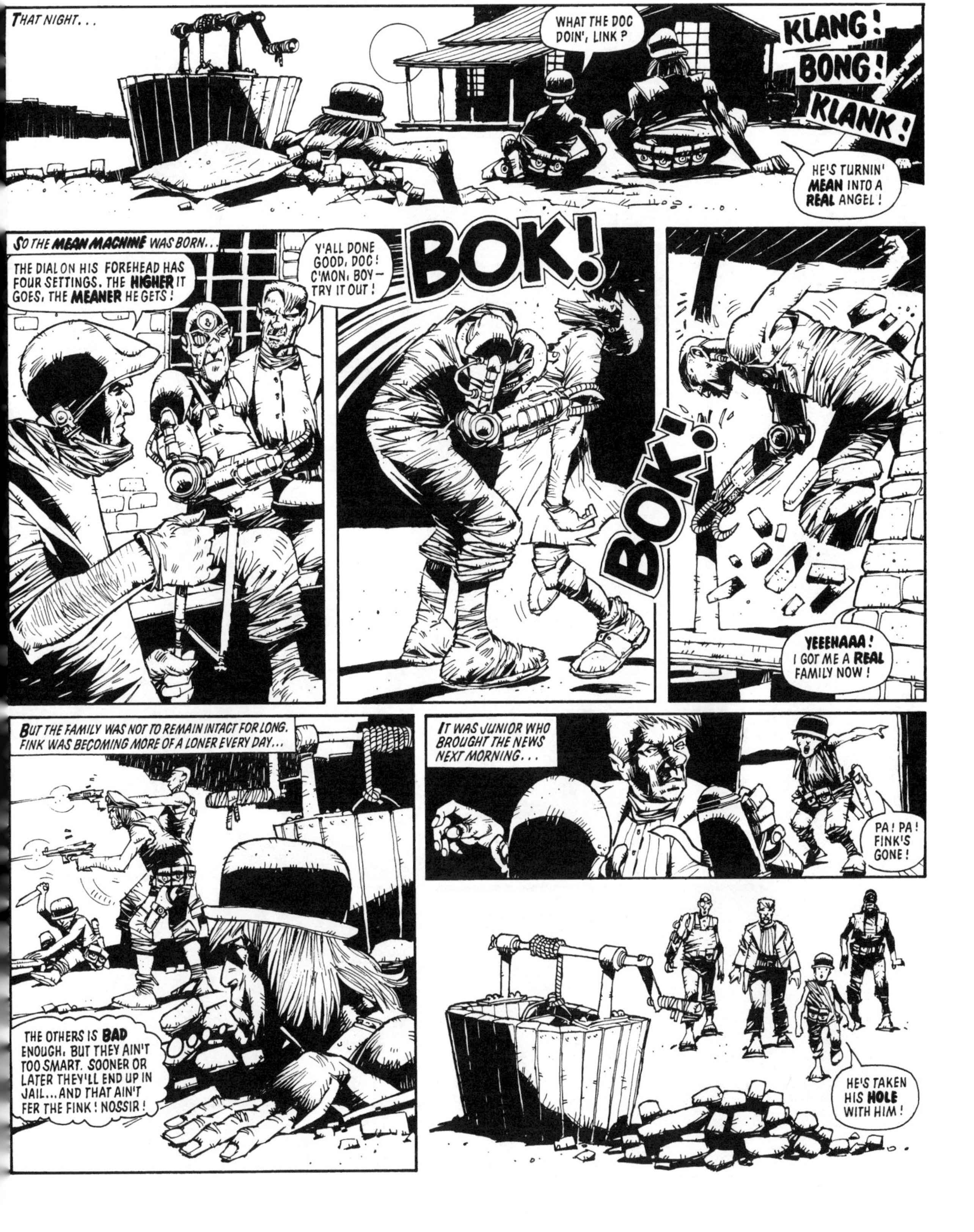

THAT NIGHT...

WHAT THE DOC DOIN', LINK?

KLANG! BONG! KLANK!

HE'S TURNIN' **MEAN** INTO A **REAL** ANGEL!

SO THE **MEAN MACHINE** WAS BORN...

THE DIAL ON HIS FOREHEAD HAS FOUR SETTINGS. THE **HIGHER** IT GOES, THE **MEANER** HE GETS!

Y'ALL DONE GOOD, DOC! C'MON, BOY— TRY IT OUT!

BOK!

BOK!

YEEEHAAA! I GOT ME A **REAL** FAMILY NOW!

AND SO FINK ANGEL BEGAN HIS CAREER AS A CURSED EARTH DESPERADO...
IT WAS HERE THAT HIS NATURAL SLYNESS AND HIS ENCYCLOPAEDIC KNOWLEDGE OF POISONS STOOD HIM IN GOOD STEAD...
WATER HOAL
REAL PURE DRINKIN WATER
I'LL USE MY GENERAL PURPOSE PIZEN!

UNWARY TRAVELLERS MADE EASY VICTIMS...
UUURRGGH...

HOWDY!

WHEN EACH SITE BECAME CLUTTERED WITH THE DEBRIS OF HIS VICTIMS, FINK WOULD MOVE ON...
AND, AS THE YEARS PASSED AND THE RADIATION TOOK ITS TOLL, HE BECAME SOMETHING LESS THAN HUMAN... LESS THAN ANIMAL! A WARPED CREATURE IN A WARPED LAND –

A DOWNRIGHT FINK!

IT WAS WHILE EXCAVATING A NEW HOLE THAT FINK MET THE CURSED EARTH RAT WHO WAS TO BECOME HIS LIFELONG FRIEND . . .

EITHER YOU'RE A-GOIN' TO BITE ME, OR I'M A-GOIN' TO BITE YOU! WHICH IS IT TO BE, RAT?

SLURP!
I THINK HE LIKES ME!

FOR MANY YEARS FINK HEARD NOTHING OF HIS FAMILY. NOR DID HE CARE. THEN, ONE DAY, A TATTERED NEWS-PAPER BLEW ACROSS HIS HOLE . . .
WHAT'S THIS, RATTY?

DREDD RETURNS FROM JUDGE CHILD MISSION:
ANGEL GANG EXECUTED
Judges Dredd, Hershey and Larter are back on street duty after the controversial end to their search for the Judge Child.
PA! THE BOYS! THEY'RE DEAD! THEM THAR JUDGES KILLED 'EM!

FINK HAD NO LOVE FOR HIS FAMILY – HE DID NOT KNOW THE MEANING OF THE WORD. BUT HE UNDERSTOOD DUTY . . . AND IT WAS HIS DUTY TO SEEK REVENGE!
NO ONE KILLS ANGELS AN' GITS AWAY WITH IT, RATTY! RECKON WE'LL MOSEY ON OVER TO MEGA-CITY ONE!

NOW THE FINK WAS IN MEGA-CITY ONE . . . AND ALREADY JUDGE LARTER WAS DEAD . . .
RECKON IT'S DARK ENOUGH, RATTY!

. . . AND JUDGE HERSHEY WOULD BE NEXT!
I GOT SOMETHIN' SPECIAL PLANNED FER YOU, WUMMAN . . . SOMETHIN' REAL SPECIAL!
NEXT PROG: THE BODY FACTORY!

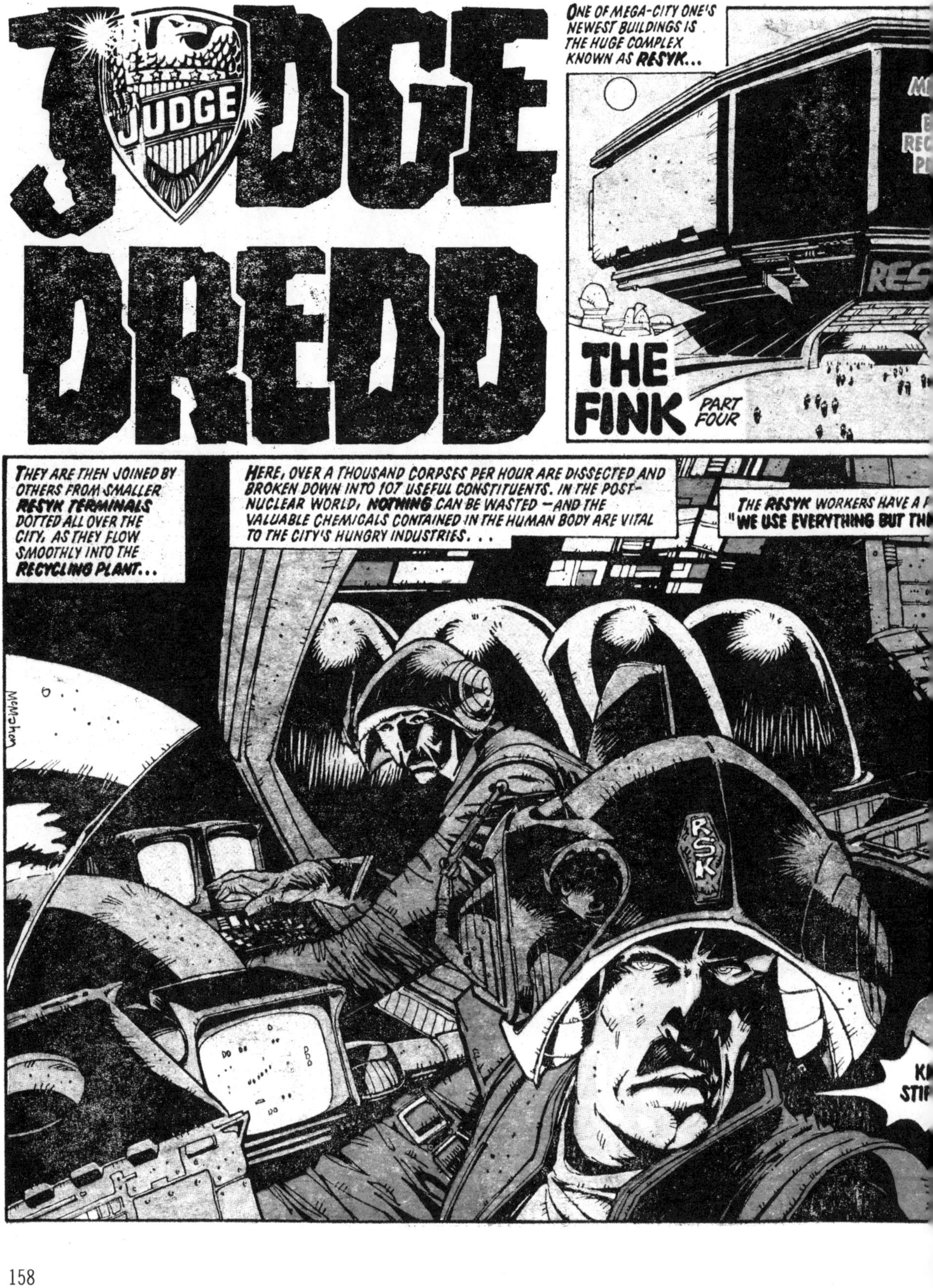

ONE OF MEGA-CITY ONE'S NEWEST BUILDINGS IS THE HUGE COMPLEX KNOWN AS RESYK...
THE FINK
PART FOUR

THEY ARE THEN JOINED BY OTHERS FROM SMALLER **RESYK TERMINALS** DOTTED ALL OVER THE CITY, AS THEY FLOW SMOOTHLY INTO THE **RECYCLING PLANT...**

HERE, OVER A THOUSAND CORPSES PER HOUR ARE DISSECTED AND BROKEN DOWN INTO 107 USEFUL CONSTITUENTS. IN THE POST-NUCLEAR WORLD, **NOTHING** CAN BE WASTED — AND THE VALUABLE CHEMICALS CONTAINED IN THE HUMAN BODY ARE VITAL TO THE CITY'S HUNGRY INDUSTRIES. . .

THE **RESYK** WORKERS HAVE A
"**WE USE EVERYTHING BUT TH**

HERE THE ELEVEN MILLION CITIZENS WHO DIE EACH YEAR FIND A LAST RESTING PLACE. . . SORT OF. . .
GOODBYE, AUBREY!
GOODBYE, ISOBEL! WAIT FOR ME IN HEAVEN!
302

ONCE THROUGH THE PLUSH SYNTHI-VELV CURTAINS, MECHANICAL HANDS REMOVE THE CORPSES AND PLACE THEM ON THE CONVEYOR BELT. . .

2000 A.D.
Credit Card:
SCRIPT ROBOT T. B. GROVER
ART ROBOT MIKE McMAHON
LETTERING ROBOT TOM FRAME
COMPU·73E

TONIGHT, SOME OF THE RESYK WORKERS THEMSELVES WILL BE JOINING THE CORPSES ON THE CONVEYOR BELT. FOR THE FINK IS IN TOWN . . .
HE HAS COME TO KILL!
STAFF ONLY
HEY! YOU CAN'T COME IN HERE!

DONK!
UGGH!

JUS' TWO OF 'EM, RATTY! MY QUICK-KILLIN' PIZEN!

WHA-?

HUH...!

DEAD AS FENCEPOSTS! RECKON WE'LL FEED 'EM TO THEIR OWN MACHINES!

Y'ALL ARE NEXT, WUMMAN- ONLY DIFFERENCE IS, YOU'RE A-GOIN' IN ALIVE!

CURSED EARTH DESPERADO FINK ANGEL HAD COME TO AVENGE THE EXECUTION OF HIS FAMILY. ALREADY JUDGE LARTER IS DEAD. NOW DREDD SEARCHES URGENTLY FOR JUDGE HERSHEY . . .
WHOLE SEWER SYSTEM CHECKED — NO SIGN OF HERSHEY!
THE FINK MUST'VE CHOSEN SOME OTHER WAY OF DISPOSING OF HER—
CONTROL TO DREDD! PRIORITY ONE!

SURVEILLANCE CAMERAS REPORT BREAK-IN AT RESYK! FEEDING PICTURES TO YOUR BIKE SCREEN.
DROKK! IT'S HIM!

RESYK ISN'T FAR! LET'S MOVE!

A STRONG PARALYSING POISON COURSED THROUGH HERSHEY'S BODY...
THERE YOU GO, JUDGE WUMMAN!
WHAT'S THAT, RATTY? TELL HER WHAT'S GOIN' TO HAPPEN TO HER? DANG TOOTIN', I WILL!

FIRST, THAT THAR MACHINE PULLS OUT YOUR TEETH AN' — POP! — PLUCKS OUT YOUR EYES! THEN SLICERS SLICE YOU RIGHT OPEN AN' SUCKERS SUCK OUT YOUR INNARDS...!
AN' IF THAT AIN'T ENOUGH, THE FLESH THAT'S LEFT GITS DISSOLVED INTO A CHEMICAL SLUDGE AN' CRUSHERS GRIND DOWN YOUR BONES FINE AS CURSED EARTH SAND! REAL NASTY, AIN'T IT?

THAT'LL LARN YOU TO GO A-KILLIN' ANGELS!
THE ONLY THING WE DID WRONG WAS KILL ONE TOO FEW!

STOP IN THE NAME OF THE LAW!

MORE JUDGES! I'LL GET 'EM, RATTY BOY!

YEEARGH!

THOSE PELLETS ARE POISONED! GOT TO DODGE THEM AND REACH THE **CONTROLS**!

WHAT A CRAZY WAY TO GO!

EMERG
STOP

THE MACHINERY GRINDS TO A SUDDEN HALT...

THIS IS JUDGE DREDD! YOU'RE UNDER ARREST, FINK ANGEL!
AAGGGH!
DREDD

HE'S RUNNING FOR COVER!

Y'ALL HEARD HIM, RATTY! THAT THAR'S **DREDD**, THE THIRD JUDGE THAT DONE KILLED PA AN' THE BOYS!
SPLIT UP! LET'S **GIT** HIM!

DROKK! LEAKING DECOMPOSING FLUID! GONNA MAKE A MESS OF THE UNIFORM...

GIVE YOURSELF UP, FINK! YOU CAN'T ESCAPE THE LAW!

FINK'S RAT!

ONE BITE FROM A CURSED EARTH RAT IS FATAL —
EAT SLUDGE, RAT!

UUHHH!

MY BEST PARALYZIN' PIZEN, LAWMAN! YOU'LL BE STIFF AS A BOARD IN TWO SHAKES, THEN Y'ALL KIN JOIN THE WUMMAN JUDGE!

WITH ONE LAST EFFORT, DREDD SWINGS HIS LEADEN ARM —
RATTY!

YAARRGH!

OTHER JUDGES ARE SOON ON THE SCENE —
WHAT A MESS! GET THE MEDI-SQUADS IN HERE!

DURING THE FIGHT, THE FEEDER CONVEYORS HAD CONTINUED TO FUNCTION —
BETTER GET SOME RESYK BOYS ON THE JOB AND QUICK! THE BODIES ARE PILING UP!

NEXT DAY, DREDD IS WELL ON THE WAY TO RECOVERY —
THE MED TEKS SAY FINK IS STILL ALIVE! GUESS IT TAKES A CREEP LIKE HIM TO SURVIVE A CURSED EARTH RAT BITE!
LET'S SEE HOW HE SURVIVES LIFE IN AN ISOLATION CUBE!

FROM WHAT I'VE SEEN OF HIM, HE'LL PROBABLY LIKE IT!

FOOTNOTE:
RATTY WAS NEVER CAPTURED. NOW HE LIVES IN RESYK, WHERE HE HAS A COMFORTABLE NEST AND AN ABUNDANT SUPPLY OF FOOD...
THOUGH NATURALLY HE MISSES HIS OLD FRIEND FINK, IN OTHER RESPECTS HE'S DOING VERY NICELY, THANK YOU.
THE END

STAPLES

WHERE DO I STAND?
I'LL TELL YOU WHERE I STAND.
I STAND FOUR-SQUARE FOR JUSTICE. I STAND FOR DISCIPLINE, GOOD ORDER AND THE RIGID APPLICATION OF THE LAW — AND GRUD HELP ANY LIMP-WRIST LIBERALS WHO SAY DIFFERENT.
THE PEOPLE, THEY KNOW WHERE I STAND. THEY NEED RULES TO LIVE BY — I PROVIDE THEM. THEY BREAK THE RULES, I BREAK THEM. THAT'S THE WAY IT WORKS.
THE PEOPLE LIKE IT THAT WAY. THEY NEED TO KNOW WHERE THEY STAND.
RIGHTS?
SURE. I'M ALL FOR RIGHTS. BUT NOT AT THE EXPENSE OF ORDER.
THAT'S WHY I LIKE TO SEE THAT STATUE OF JUDGEMENT STANDING THERE, TOWERING OVER LIBERTY.
KIND OF A SYMBOL.

JUSTICE HAS A PRICE.
THE PRICE IS FREEDOM.

THIS IS A LOVE STORY.
I'M GOING TO TELL YOU HOW I LOVED A WOMAN... LOVED HER FROM THE FIRST MOMENT I CAN REMEMBER— LOVE HER STILL, THOUGH THE SPARK THAT ANIMATED HER HAS LONG SINCE BEEN CRUSHED OUT.
TALK OF THE MEG
BENNETT BEENY
AND I'LL TELL YOU HOW I BETRAYED HER — AND WHEN I'VE FINISHED YOU'LL DESPISE ME FOR WHAT I DID.

I WAS FOOLISH THEN. I DIDN'T—OR WOULDN'T UNDERSTAND...
BUT I'M NOT TRYING TO EXCUSE MYSELF. PLEASE, HATE AWAY. I DESERVE IT.

THE MEG
BENNETT BEENY
THOUGH WHETHER ANY MAN DESERVES THE PUNISHMENT I INFLICTED ON MYSELF... ONLY YOU CAN JUDGE.

AMERICA.
TODAY HER EYES STARE BACK AT ME, SAD AND EMPTY... NO TRACE NOW OF THE FIRE THAT ONCE BURNED SO FIERCE IN THEM.

BUT I REMEMBER AMERICA.

I WAS THERE. FROM FIRST TO LAST. FROM THE MOMENT SHE CAME HOWLING INTO THIS SICK WORLD...
I WAS THERE, AT THE BIRTHDAY PARTY...
MADRE GRODDO—!!
PUSH, ALVIRA!

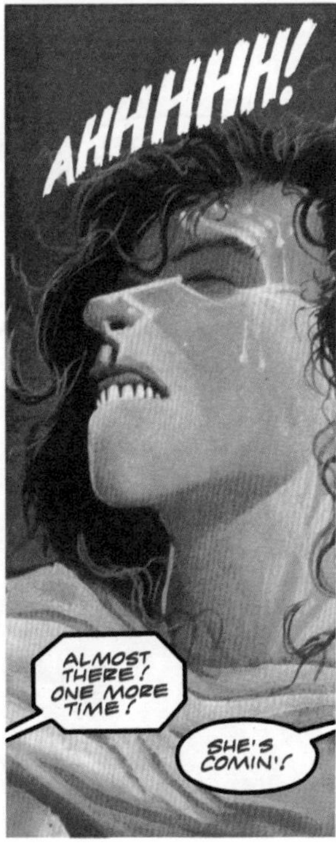
AHHHHHH!
ALMOST THERE! ONE MORE TIME!
SHE'S COMIN'!

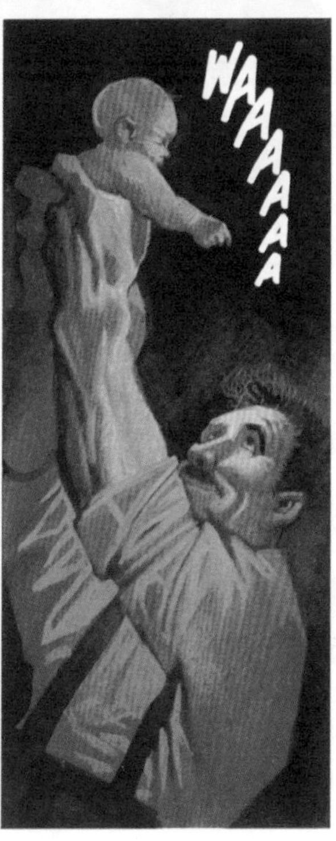
WAAAAAAAA

WONDERFUL, MRS. JARA! WONDERFUL!

WAY TO GO, ALVIRA!

CLAP CLAP!

CLAP CLAP!

Pheeep!

LOOK AT 'ER! EES THAT NO' A BEAUTIFUL GIRL, EH? EES THAT NO' A BEAUTIFUL GIRL!

A NEW FRIEND FOR YOU, BENNY!

WHAT ARE YOU GOING TO CALL HER, MR. JARA?

WELL, I TELL YOU! WE COME HERE, WE JOS' POOR DUMB IMMIES. WE GOT NOTHIN'. THEES CITY, SHE TAKE US EEN — GEEV US SHELTER.

I MEAN, WE STILL AIN'T GOT MOCH, MAN, BOT AT LEAST WE GOT HOPE. WE GOT PROSPECTS! WE ARE HERE—**AMERICA**— THE LAN' O' THE FREE AN' THE BRAVE!

AN' EEN HONOUR OF OUR NEW HOME, THAT'S WHA' WE GONNA CALL HER—

AMERICA!

...HAPPY BIRTHDAY TO YOU HAPPY BIRTHDAY, AMERICA—
AMERICA... HOW LIKE HER NAME HER LIFE WOULD BE, THOUGH WE DIDN'T KNOW IT THEN. BORN IN HOPE, WITH A DREAM — DIED IN DISILLUSIONMENT — AND DESPAIR.
LEESEN TO HER! GOT A LOT TO SAY FOR HERSELF ALREADY! SHE GONNA GO FAR, THEES ONE!
AMERICA! AMERICA! GOD SHED HEES GRIEF ON THEE!
THAT'S "GRACE", MR JARA.
EH?
NOT GRIEF— IT'S GRACE. GOD SHED HIS GRACE ON THEE.
OH, YES... SI, SI.
GRACE.

SPUG FACE!
SPUG FACE!
SPUG FACE!
SPUG FACE!
SPUG FA

BENNY!
SPUG FACE
SPUG FACE
SPUG FACE
SPUG FACE
SPUG FA

JUDGE COMIN'! SCRAMOLA!

YOU SCUMMERS! DON'T YOU EVER COME BACK HERE AGAIN!

TH-THEY BROKE MY GITTER...
DON'T CRY, BENNY. I'LL BUY YOU A NEW ONE.
TH-THEY COST AN AWFUL LOT, AMI...

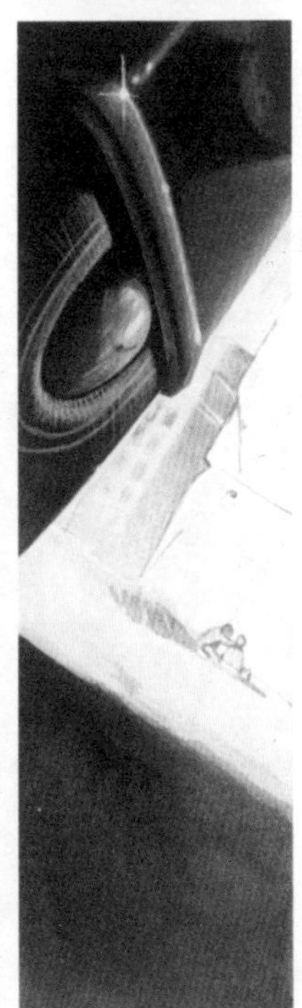

I CAN'T REMEMBER WHEN I FIRST BECAME AWARE OF THE JUDGES.

I SUPPOSE IT'S BECAUSE THEY WERE ALWAYS THERE, A DARK PRESENCE IN THE BACKGROUND OF OUR LIVES —AS MUCH A PART OF GROWING UP AS THE AIR THAT WE BREATHED AND THE STREETS THAT WE PLAYED ON.

WHEREVER WE WENT THEY WERE THERE. WATCHING. ALWAYS WATCHING.
THEY COULD FIX YOU WITH A SPECIAL KIND OF STARE, LIKE THEY COULD LOOK RIGHT INTO YOUR SOUL.

DULTS, THEY'D TELL US THE JUDGES WERE THERE FOR OUR GOOD, TO PROTECT US AND MAKE OUR STREETS SAFE.

BUT WE'D HEAR THE TREMOR IN THEIR VOICES WHEN THEY TALKED ABOUT THEM AND SEE THEIR FURTIVE EXPRESSIONS WHENEVER A JUDGE CAUGHT THEIR EYE— AND WE'D KNOW THEY WERE AFRAID.

AND AT NIGHT MOTHERS WOULD TUCK US IN WITH DIRE WARNINGS— SLEEP OR THE JUDGES WOULD COME FOR US.

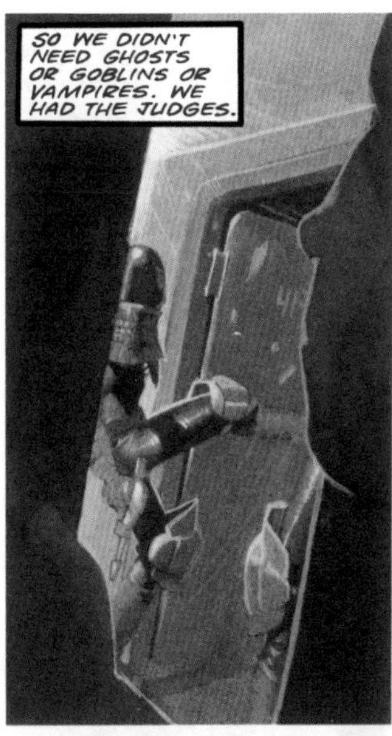
SO WE DIDN'T NEED GHOSTS OR GOBLINS OR VAMPIRES. WE HAD THE JUDGES.

AND THEY WERE WORSE.

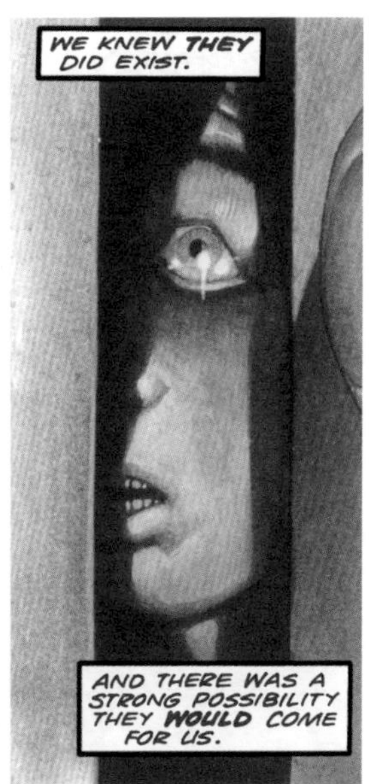
WE KNEW THEY DID EXIST.
AND THERE WAS A STRONG POSSIBILITY THEY WOULD COME FOR US.

SO I DON'T REMEMBER WHEN I BECAME AWARE OF THEM, BUT I DO REMEMBER MY FIRST ENCOUNTER. MY STOMACH STILL KNOTS UP WHEN I THINK OF IT. TO THIS SINGLE MOMENT I ATTRIBUTE MY LIFELONG TERROR OF AUTHORITY.

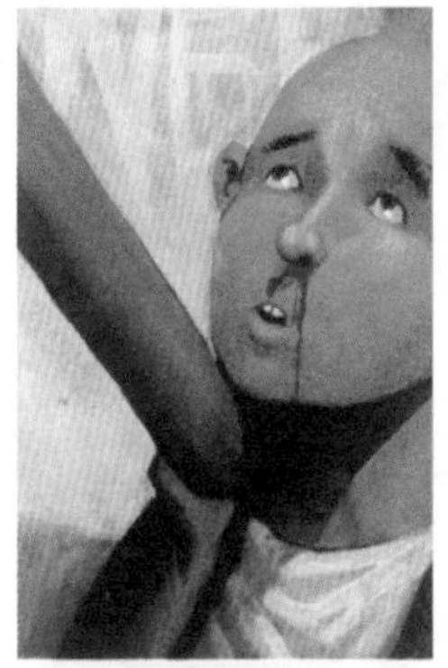

NAME?

B-BENNETT BEENY, SIR. APARTMENT 41-30, FRED NIETZSCHE.

BEEN FIGHTING, SON?
Y-YES, SIR...
YOU LIKE FIGHTING?
N-N-NO, SIR...

WE'VE GOT PLACES WE PUT BOYS WHO FIGHT. YOU WANT TO GO TO THE JUVE CUBES, SON?
N-NO, SIR...!
LOCKED UP, ALL BY YOURSELF—
N-NO!

BY GRUD, IF I THOUGHT YOU WERE A TROUBLEMAKER--
ARE YOU A TROUBLE-MAKER, SON?
N-N-NO! PLEASE—! I'M NOT A TROUBLE-MAKER!

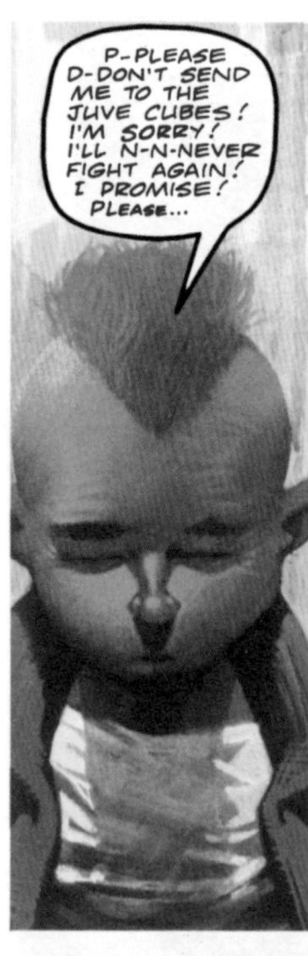
P-PLEASE D-DON'T SEND ME TO THE JUVE CUBES! I'M SORRY! I'LL N-N-NEVER FIGHT AGAIN! I PROMISE! PLEASE...

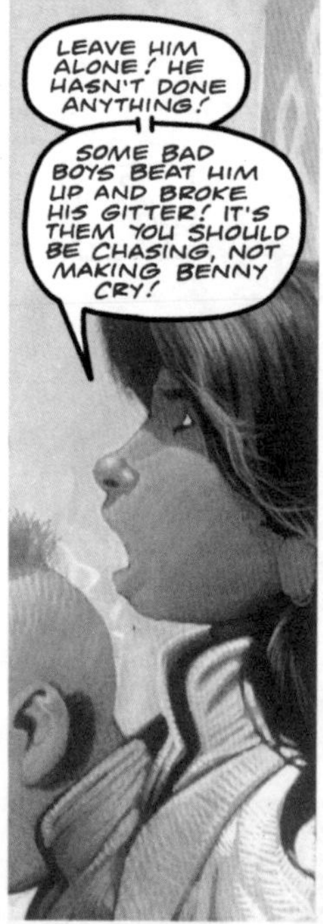
LEAVE HIM ALONE! HE HASN'T DONE ANYTHING!
SOME BAD BOYS BEAT HIM UP AND BROKE HIS GITTER! IT'S THEM YOU SHOULD BE CHASING, NOT MAKING BENNY CRY!

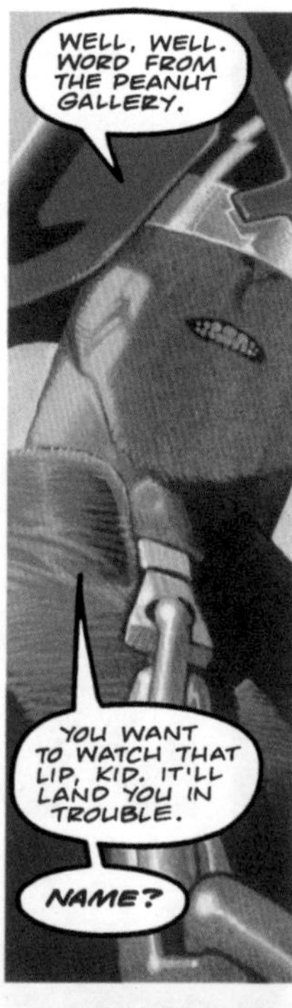
WELL, WELL. WORD FROM THE PEANUT GALLERY.
YOU WANT TO WATCH THAT LIP, KID. IT'LL LAND YOU IN TROUBLE.
NAME?

MY NAME IS AMERICA JARA. I LIVE AT APARTMENT 41-31, FRED NIETZSCHE BLOCK— AND I CAN SAY WHAT I LIKE 'COS MY DAD SAYS THIS IS AMERICA AND IT'S A FREE COUNTRY.

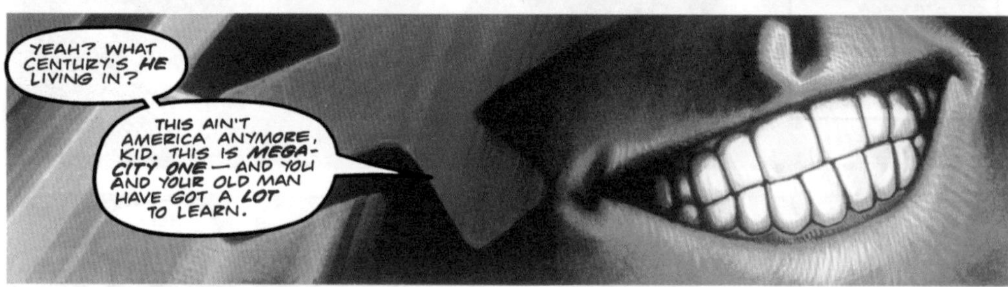
YEAH? WHAT CENTURY'S HE LIVING IN?
THIS AIN'T AMERICA ANYMORE, KID. THIS IS MEGA-CITY ONE — AND YOU AND YOUR OLD MAN HAVE GOT A LOT TO LEARN.

CONTROL, WHAT WE GOT ON A BEENY, BENNETT — TWO "T"S — OR JARA, AMERICA — THAT'S A-M-E-R-I-C-A — BOTH RESIDENTS FRED NIETZSCHE? POSSIBLE YP OFFENDERS.
NEGATIVE ON BOTH. BOY'S FATHER ONE EGGAR J. BEENY, DECEASED. VICTIM OF SERIAL KILLER, DAVID DUCHESSE.
I REMEMBER... DAVE THE ORTHODONTIST.
CHECK. STILL GOT BEENY SENIOR'S TEETH IN THE BLACK MUSEUM, IF YOU WANT THEM.
JARA FAMILY ARE IMMIGRANTS, PUERTO RICAN WASTES, STILL DOING TWENTY YEAR PROBATIONARY PERIOD. GIRL'S A LEGAL CITIZEN THOUGH.
NO DUMPING
BY ORDER

HE TOOK A DESCRIPTION OF THE JUVES. I'VE OFTEN WONDERED IF HE EVER CAUGHT THEM.
I DON'T SUPPOSE IT MATTERS.

DON'T WORRY, BENNY. HE CAN'T DO ANYTHING TO YOU.

STRANGE, HOW TWO PEOPLE CAN BE SO DIFFERENT, YET SO CLOSE.
AMI—BRIGHT AS A BUTTON, AFRAID OF NO-ONE. SHE WAS THE STRONG ONE. SHE NEVER CRIED. SOMEHOW IT ALWAYS SEEMED TO BE ME WHO ENDED IN TEARS...
WH-WHAT IF HE TELLS MY MUM?
SHE WON'T SAY ANYTHING. YOU DIDN'T DO ANYTHING WRONG.

BUT WE MADE HER CRY, IN THE END. ME AND THE JUDGES.
OH, YES. WE GOT TO HER... IN THE END.
HE WAS A BAD MAN, BENNY.

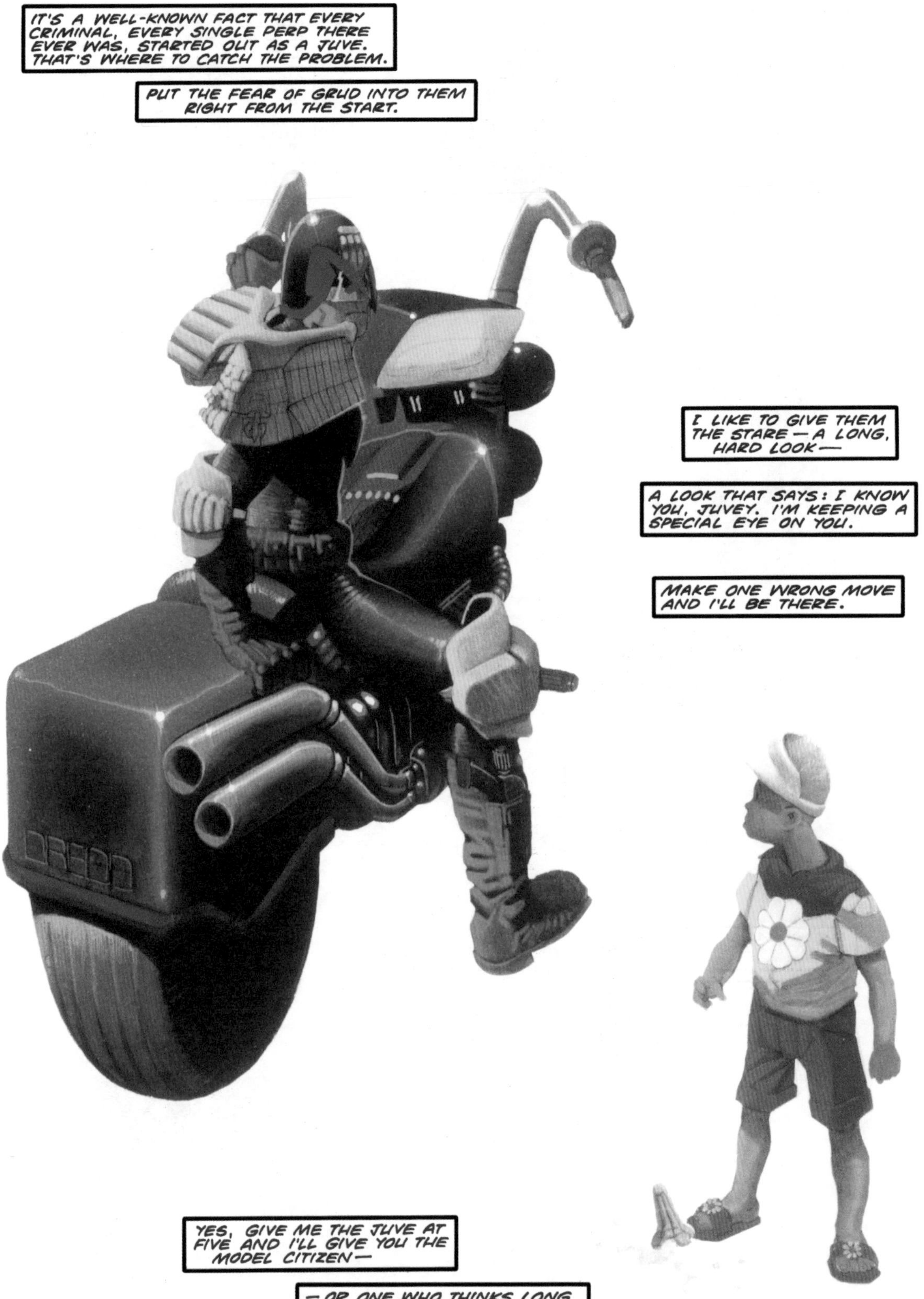

IT'S A WELL-KNOWN FACT THAT EVERY CRIMINAL, EVERY SINGLE PERP THERE EVER WAS, STARTED OUT AS A JUVE. THAT'S WHERE TO CATCH THE PROBLEM.

PUT THE FEAR OF GRUD INTO THEM RIGHT FROM THE START.

I LIKE TO GIVE THEM THE STARE — A LONG, HARD LOOK—

A LOOK THAT SAYS: I KNOW YOU, JUVEY. I'M KEEPING A SPECIAL EYE ON YOU.

MAKE ONE WRONG MOVE AND I'LL BE THERE.

YES, GIVE ME THE JUVE AT FIVE AND I'LL GIVE YOU THE MODEL CITIZEN—

—OR ONE WHO THINKS LONG AND HARD BEFORE HE STEPS OVER THE LINE.

Thomas Jefferson 1743-1826
LIFE—LIBERTY—THE PURSUIT OF HAPPINESS—THESE THREE GREAT PRINCIPLES UPON WHICH OUR ANCIENT NATION WAS FOUNDED.
LIFE : LIBERTY : PURSUIT OF H
SO WHAT HAPPENED?
I'M SORRY, AMERICA--?
WHERE'S LIBERTY GONE?
I MEAN, YOU DROP A PIECE OF LITTER AND THE JUDGES CAN LOCK YOU UP FOR IT. JAYWALK AND IT'S PRACTICALLY A CAPITAL OFFENCE.
SHE'S OFF AGAIN—!
SHUT UP, GOBBER!
THEY CAN BREAK INTO YOUR HOME ANY TIME THEY LIKE. THEY CAN BEAT YOU UP AND TORTURE YOU—
COME NOW, I THINK YOU'RE EXAGGERATING
—AND GRUD HELP YOU IF YOUR GENETIC CODE DOESN'T MATCH UP TO THEIR HIGH STANDARDS! THEY CALL YOU MUTIE AND BOOT YOU OUT OF THE CITY!
THINGS HAVE CHANGED SINCE THE DECLARATION OF INDEPENDENCE. THERE'S A PERFECTLY GOOD REASON FOR EVERYTHING.
SO MUCH FOR LIBERTY AND THE PURSUIT OF HAPPINESS!
AND HAPPINESS—THERE'S A JOKE! LOOK AROUND YOU! YOU SEE ANY HAPPY FACES?
I'M HAPPY, MAN.
YEAH, 'COS YOU'RE DRUNK.
AT LEAST WE'RE STILL ALIVE, AMERICA. ONE OUT OF THREE'S NOT BAD.

WHO JUDGES THE JUDGES?
IT MAKES ME SO **MAD**, BENNY!
JUSTICE DEPT. WARNING TO LEAPERS
HOW DID THE JUDGES GET ALL THAT POWER? THEY JUST **TOOK** IT! AND NOBODY SEEMS TO GIVE A DAMN!
C'MON, CAN YOU BLAME THEM? WHO WANTS TO TAKE ON JUSTICE DEPARTMENT? IT'S A LOT EASIER JUST TO PLAY IT THEIR WAY. YOU KNOW--
I'M A MEAN OLD JUDGE, MY NAME IS DREDD, DO WHAT YOU'RE TOLD OR I'LL BUST YOUR HEAD! DON'T TALK OF FREEDOM, FREEDOM IS FOR FOOLS, YOU'LL DO MUCH BETTER TO OBEY THESE RULES—
BOW DOWN AND KNUCKLE UNDER! YOU'LL FIND I'M VERY FAIR! SO LONG AS YOU REMEMBER—
JUST PLANT YOUR LIPS RIGHT THERE!
SHE LAUGHED. I CAN PICTURE HER STILL, HER FACE ALL AGLOW. HOW BEAUTIFUL SHE WAS.
DID YOU JUST MAKE THAT UP?

SHE LAUGHED SO LITTLE THOSE DAYS. LIFE WAS ALWAYS SO SERIOUS.
YOU'RE A NATURAL COMIC, BENNY. YOU'VE GOT A REAL TALENT FOR IT...
I JUST WISH I COULD SEE THE FUNNY SIDE OF IT...

DON'T YOU SEE, PEOPLE CAME TO AMERICA TO **ESCAPE** FROM TYRANNY, TO BE FREE, TO HAVE THE RIGHT TO DECIDE FOR THEMSELVES HOW THEY WANTED TO LIVE.
THE JUDGES HAVE TAKEN ALL THAT AWAY FROM US AND NOTHING WILL EVER CHANGE UNLESS WE'RE PREPARED TO **DO** SOMETHING ABOUT IT— STAND UP AND TELL THEM TO KEEP THE HELL **OUT** OF OUR LIVES!

I'M DOING SOMETHING.
JEEZ, AMI! PUT THEM AWAY!

POSTING BILLS FOR THE DEMOCRATS— ARE YOU **CRAZY**? THEY CAN LOCK YOU UP FOR THAT!
NOT FOR POSSESSION.
THEY'LL GET YOU ON A BILL-STICKING RAP. YOU KNOW HOW THEY WORK.
JEEZ... THE **DEMS**! I DON'T BELIEVE IT! YOU START MIXING WITH THEM YOU'RE **ASKING** FOR TROUBLE!

I BEGGED HER TO STOP. I TRIED TO MAKE HER SEE YOU COULD PLAY IT BY THEIR RULES AND STILL LIVE A GOOD LIFE...
YOU'RE WRONG. LIFE, LIBERTY, THE PURSUIT OF HAPPINESS — THEY'RE NOT JUST EMPTY WORDS. THEY MATTER. PEOPLE **DIED** TO MAKE SURE THEY'D ALWAYS BE OURS BY **RIGHT**.

WE CAN DO ALMOST ANYTHING, BENNY... WE CAN FLY, WE CAN TRAVEL TO THE STARS. ARE THEY GOING TO TELL US WE'RE NOT CAPABLE OF TAKING CONTROL OF OUR OWN LIVES..?

THE JUDGES, THEY'RE LIKE A STRAIT-JACKET— THROW THEM OFF AND WE'LL BE FREE AGAIN. IT'S IN OUR HANDS. WE CAN DO IT, IF WE JUST WANT IT ENOUGH.

HOW I LOVED HER, WANTED TO PROTECT HER, TO SAVE HER FROM THE DANGER SHE WAS RUSHING HEADLONG INTO.

I WENT WITH HER ONCE... THREE HOURS OF GUT-WRENCHING TERROR.

SHE NEVER ASKED ME TO GO AGAIN, AND I WAS GRATEFUL.

BY 15 SHE'D PICKED UP HER FIRST CONVICTION — ILLEGAL POSTING. THREE MONTHS JUVE CUBES PLUS MANDATORY REHAB. SHE WAS STARTING TO BE A MARKED TROUBLEMAKER.

SHE'D COME OUT OF THE CLOSET, HANGING ROUND WITH ALL THE DEMMY CROWD AND FLAUNTING DEM STICKERS ON HER BAG.

SOMEWHERE ALONG THE WAY CHILDHOOD ENDED. AMI AND I WERE DRIFTING APART. I WATCHED IT HAPPENING, HATING IT, POWERLESS TO PREVENT IT.
OH, AMI, COWARD THAT I AM I'D HAVE JOINED THE DAMNED DEMS IF IT MEANT I COULD HAVE HAD YOU. I'D HAVE MARCHED WITH YOU AND FOUGHT WITH YOU AND DIED WITH YOU...
YET PART OF ME ALWAYS KNEW IT WAS ONLY A DREAM, A FOOL'S DREAM. SHE WAS LIGHT AND FIRE AND LIGHTNING. AND ME — JUST DULL OLD BENNY BEENY.
THE FLAME THAT BURNED IN AMERICA WAS TOO BRIGHT FOR ME EVER TO HOLD.

FRIED... NIETZSCHE BLOCK
I'D SEE HER TURNING HEADS AS WE PASSED, TALL AND PROUD AND SELF-CONFIDENT IN HER GROWING WOMANHOOD— FEELING STRANGELY PRIVILEGED TO BE WITH HER, TO BE SHARING HER SPACE, SHARING THE SAME PLANET.
I'D WATCH HER WITH HER NEW FRIENDS, FEELING FOR THE FIRST TIME LIKE AN OUTSIDER.
LOVING HER, LONGING FOR HER.
AND TOO AFRAID TO TELL HER.
KNOWING WHAT HER ANSWER WOULD BE.
IF I SAID NOTHING, AT LEAST THERE WAS ALWAYS HOPE...
HOPE ENDED TWO WEEKS BEFORE THE GRADUATION BOP...
I'M SORRY, BENNY— I ALREADY SAID I'D GO WITH DOODY.
DOODY MANSON? JEEZ, AMI! HE'S HEAVY IN WITH THE DEMOCRATS! HELL, THE GUY'S ALREADY SPENT HALF HIS LIFE IN JUVE REHAB!
HE'S NO GOOD FOR YOU—HE'S TROUBLE! I'M THE ONE. I LOVE YOU.
THEN IT ALL CAME POURING OUT, DUMB WORD STUMBLING AFTER DUMB WORD —AND ALL THE TIME I COULD SEE THE ANSWER WRITTEN ON HER FACE.
OH, BENNY... I LOVE YOU TOO, BUT... NOT THAT WAY...
I KNOW. LIKE A BROTHER, HUH?
WELL, AMI, I GOTTA GO.
BENNY...
BENNY!
I DO LOVE YOU, HONEST I DO.
PLEASE DON'T CRY...
OH, BENNY.

I WENT TO THE BOP. ALONE.
BOP
I HAD TO ADMIT, AMI AND DOODY LOOKED GOOD TOGETHER.
THEY ASKED ME TO SING A COUPLE OF MY COMEDY SONGS. I DID "THE GEEK WHO ATE MY KNEEPAD" AND "THE LIMPTY MAN."
EVERYBODY LAUGHED.
EXCEPT THE COMEDIAN.
AMI WENT AWAY TO WEST SECTOR U — POLITICS. DOODY WENT TOO. SHE PROMISED SHE'D WRITE REGULARLY AND SHE DID. SHE TOLD ME SHE AND DOODY WERE SHARING A STUDEHAB.
THERE'S HARDLY ROOM FOR ONE IN A STUDEHAB. I DIDN'T WANT TO KNOW ANY MORE.

MY MOM DIED. TERMINAL BOREDOM, THEY SAID. AMI COULDN'T MAKE IT TO RESYK— SOME STUDE PROTEST.
MC-1 BODY RECYCLING PLANT
RESYK
WOULD YOU LIKE TO SEE HER ON THE BELT?
THEY SAY IT HELPS SOMETIMES—
WHAT..?
—TO KNOW OUR DEAR ONES ARE BEING PUT TO GOOD USE. IN DEATH, AS THEY NEVER COULD IN LIFE...
OH... SURE...

LIFE SHE EES SAD, EH, BENNY?
WHAT YOU GONNA DO NOW?

I'VE BEEN HAVING SOME SUCCESS WITH MY MUSIC.
AH, YES, SI! WE HEAR! YOU GONNA BE THE BEEG STAR, EH? MRS BEENY'S LEETLE BOY GONNA MAKE EET BEEG.
YOUR MOMMA, SHE BE PROUD OF YOU.

ME, I NO' HAPPY HERE. EES NO WHAT I THEENK.
DANGER
"HEY, YOU, PICK OP THAT PAPER— HEY, YOU, STOP STANDING THERE— HEY, YOU, OP AGAINST THE WALL!"
NO DO ANYTHING —NO WORK—TAKE ONE STEP OUT OF LINE AN' BANG! YOU DEAD!

I WEESH WE NEVER COME... EES NO' THE GREAT DREAM PLACE— EES NO AMERICA NO MORE.

I'M WORRIED ABOUT HER, BENNY. SHE NO COME HOME NO MORE— SHE EEN BEEG WITH THESE DEMOCRATS. AN' THAT DOOD GUY—!
NO GOOD GONNA COME OF EET, BOT WHAT CAN YOU DO? AMERICA, SHE GONNA DO WHAT SHE LIKE, WHATEVER YOU SAY...
YES...

I WROTE TO HER THAT NIGHT.
I STILL HAVE THE LETTER.
SHE'D KEPT IT.

Dear Ami,
Now mom's gone there's no reason for me to hang around old Fred Neitzsche. So I guess this is goodbye. I don't think I'll write any more. I'm sure you understand.
I just want you to know that I'll always love you. If you ever need me, I'm there.
Take care of yourself
Benny

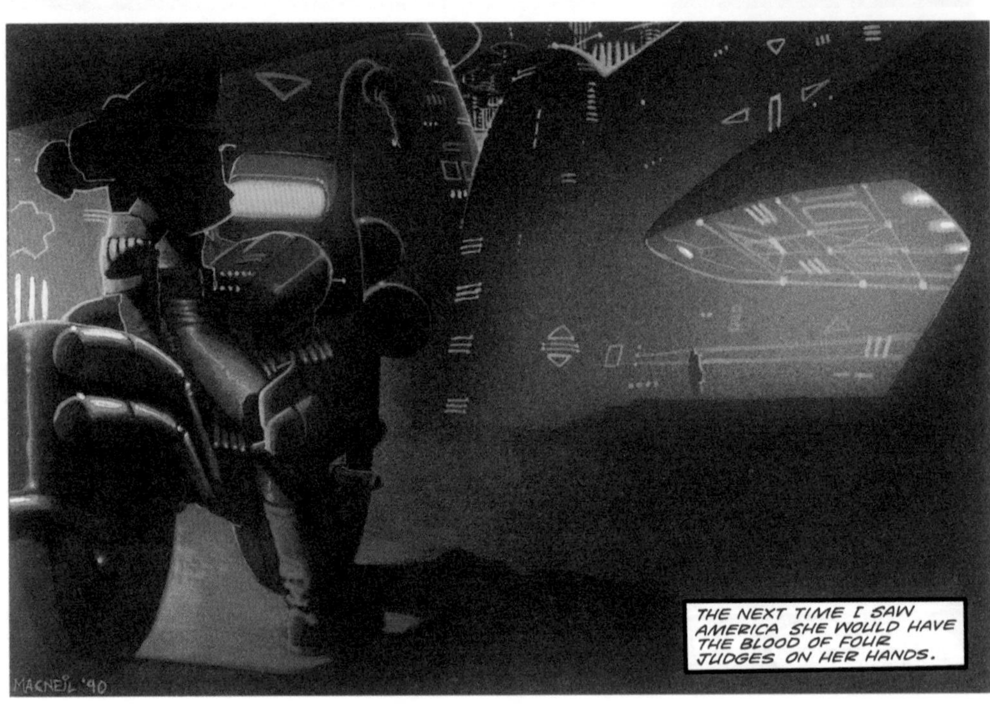

THE NEXT TIME I SAW AMERICA SHE WOULD HAVE THE BLOOD OF FOUR JUDGES ON HER HANDS.
MACNEIL '90

THE WAR CAME.
I WAS IN MEGA-CITY TWO WHEN IT STARTED. I SAT IT OUT THERE.

WHEN IT WAS OVER I LOOKED FOR AMI AT WEST SECTOR U.

STUDEHAB UNIT K
NO RECORDS REMAINED.

OLD FRED NIETZSCHE HAD MADE IT THROUGH...
THE JARAS— THEY USED TO LIVE NEXT DOOR...
THEY HAD A DAUGHTER— AMERICA.

I DON' REMEMBER NO AMERICA BUT I REMEMBER THE GUY, ALL RIGHT. KILLED HISSELF— WENT MAD WIT' A STANLEY LASER. GOT HIS WIFE AN' A FEW A' THE NEIGHBOURS, THEN TRIED TO GIVE HISSELF A APPENDICKAMY.

GOT ME AS WELL.
'COURSE, I DIDN'T CARE. I WAS PRETTY CRAZY TOO— BLOCK MANIA.

I'M STILL A LITTLE LOOPY.
HEY—AIN'T YOU BENNETT BEENY? YOU USED TA LIVE HERE, DINCHA?

YEAH, I SEEN YOU ONNA VID THE OTHER NIGHT! I THOUGHT YOU WUZ CRAP BUT THE DOG LIKED YA.
HEY, HOW ABOUT YOUR AUTOGRAPH, MAN?

HEY, C'MON! I GOT MY OWN STANLEY! YOU CAN PUT IT RIGHT THERE!

AMI'S NAME DIDN'T APPEAR ON ANY DP LIST, AND AFTER THAT I STOPPED LOOKING. IN A WAY I SUPPOSE I WAS GLAD NOT TO FIND HER. IT WOULD ONLY HAVE BROUGHT BACK ALL THE HURT AND THE PAIN.

SO I HOPED THAT SHE WAS ALIVE, AND I WISHED HER WELL. AND NOT A DAY PASSED WHEN I DIDN'T THINK OF HER.

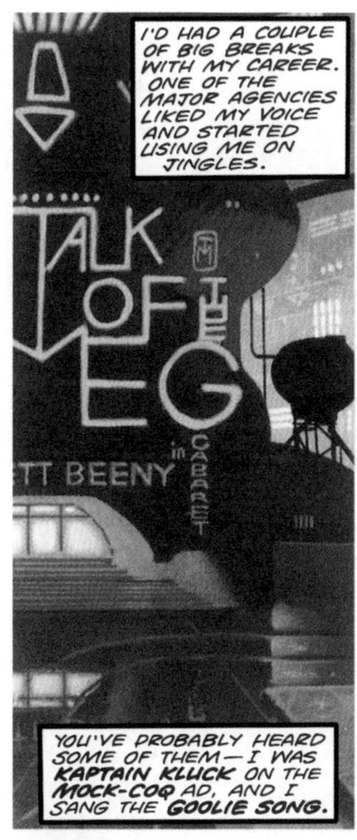
I'D HAD A COUPLE OF BIG BREAKS WITH MY CAREER. ONE OF THE MAJOR AGENCIES LIKED MY VOICE AND STARTED USING ME ON JINGLES.
TALK OF THE MEG
in CABARET
TT BEENY
YOU'VE PROBABLY HEARD SOME OF THEM—I WAS KAPTAIN KLUCK ON THE MOCK-COQ AD, AND I SANG THE GOOLIE SONG.

JERALDO SAYS FIVE MINUTES.

RANDY SEER-SUCKER HEARD ONE OF MY COMEDY NUMBERS ON A DEMO SLUG AND GAVE ME A SPOT ON TONY TUBBS' SHOW. THEY LIKED ME. MY FREIDBACH RATING WAS 79. A PHENOMENAL 85 AMONG WOMEN IN THE 35-54 GROUP.

IT SEEMS I AROUSED SOME MOTHERING INSTINCT.
BENNETT
SONGS OF LOVE

AFTER THAT I WAS MADE. MONEY STARTED POURING IN. I BOUGHT A BIG NIMBY UNIT ON THE RIDLEY ESTATE.
'LECTRIC WALLS TO KEEP OUT JOE CIT, DROID SERVANTS, MY OWN ANTI-GRAV POOL—A REAL GARDEN, FOR GRUD'S SAKE.

I WONDERED WHAT AMERICA WOULD SAY IF SHE COULD SEE ME NOW. MRS BEENY'S BOY—LIVING LIKE A SULTAN.
MEGA BEAT
I'D BEEN RIGHT. YOU COULD PLAY IT BY THEIR RULES AND HAVE A GOOD LIFE.

WHEN THE BIG DEMOCRATIC MARCH HAPPENED I LOOKED FOR HER. IT WAS HOPELESS, OF COURSE — ONE FACE AMONG SIXTEEN MILLION.

I PRAYED THAT SHE WASN'T ON IT.

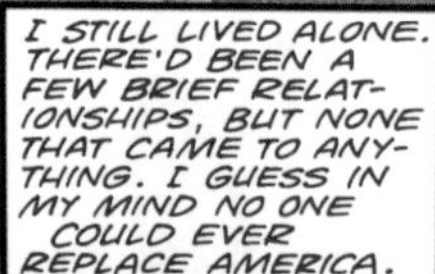
I STILL LIVED ALONE. THERE'D BEEN A FEW BRIEF RELATIONSHIPS, BUT NONE THAT CAME TO ANYTHING. I GUESS IN MY MIND NO ONE COULD EVER REPLACE AMERICA.

NOW AND THEN I SOUGHT REFUGE WITH THE LADIES OF THE SLAB...
FURTIVE, UGLY, HUMILIATING LITTLE ENCOUNTERS IN HOTEL ROOMS AND SLEEPEEZEES.

THAT'S WHERE I FOUND HER.

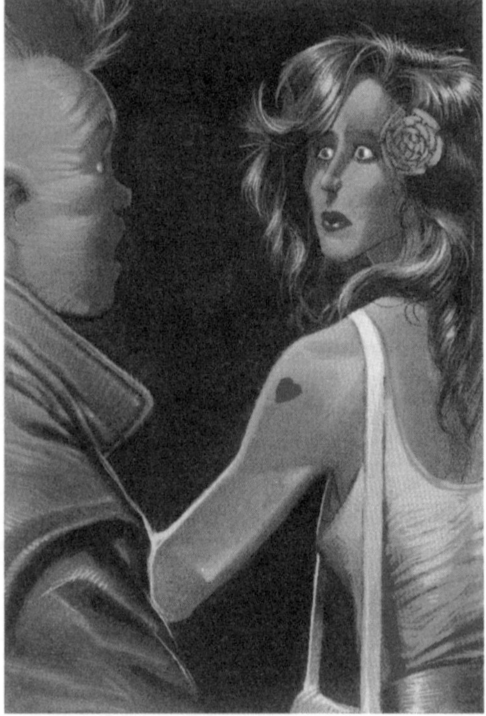

AMI!
WH-WH-WHAT ARE YOU--?
DON'T ASK, BENNY. PLEASE— JUST GO.
GRUD! THAT YOU'VE SUNK TO THIS! COULDN'T YOU HAVE COME TO ME, AMI?
BENNY, WILL YOU GET OUT OF HERE—!
AMI—?
WHAT THE HELL IS..?
SOMETHING WRONG HERE...
JUDGES..?
SET UP!
AMI—
NO!

AAAAAAAAAAA
CON...TROL...
WE GOTTA—
HUUNNNN—
GOTTA...
BASTARD!

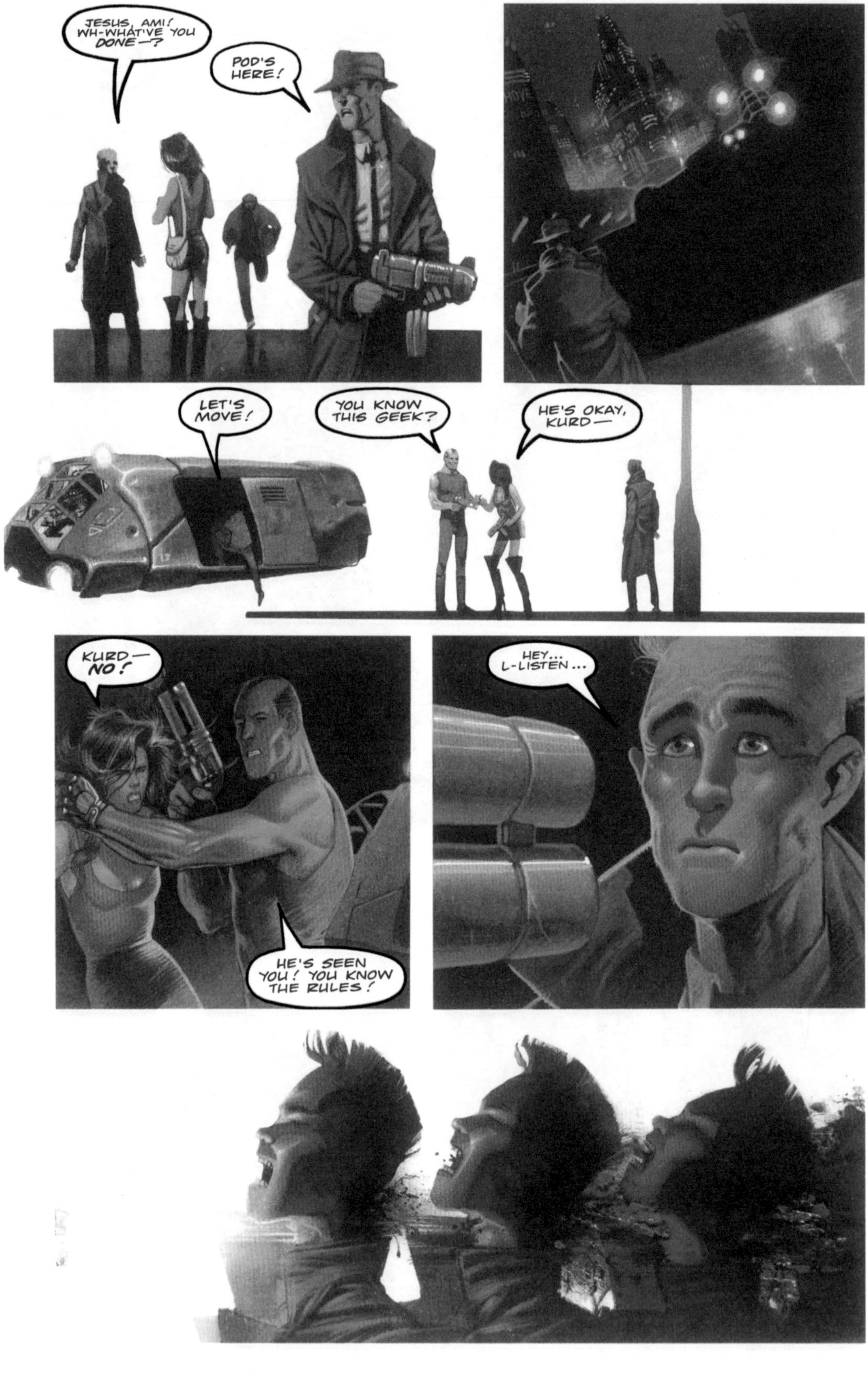

JESUS, AMI! WH-WHAT'VE YOU DONE—?
POD'S HERE!

LET'S MOVE!
YOU KNOW THIS GEEK?
HE'S OKAY, KURD—

DAMN YOU!
DAMN YOU!
SHUT UP!
GET IN!

GO!

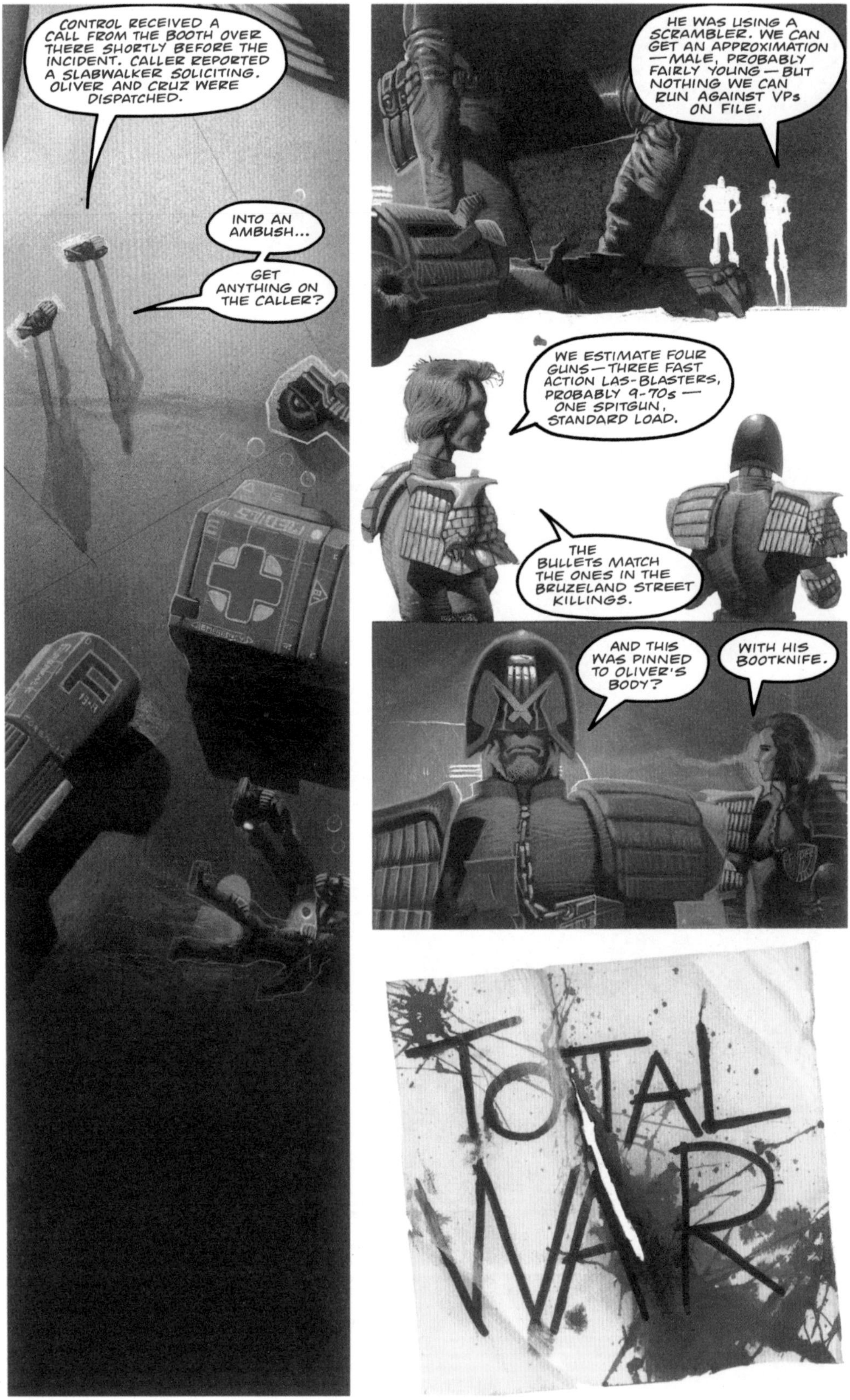

CONTROL RECEIVED A CALL FROM THE BOOTH OVER THERE SHORTLY BEFORE THE INCIDENT. CALLER REPORTED A SLABWALKER SOLICITING. OLIVER AND CRUZ WERE DISPATCHED.

INTO AN AMBUSH...

GET ANYTHING ON THE CALLER?

THAT REALLY BENNETT BEENY?
WHAT WAS HE DOING HERE? THE SLABWALKER?
COULD BE. CAN'T SEE HIM TIED IN WITH THIS TOTAL WAR BUNCH, THAT'S FOR SURE...
THAT'S HIS POD PARKED UP THE STREET.
YOU EVER HEAR HIM?
I KNOW THE NAME. JUST ANOTHER CREEP.
HE WAS ACTUALLY QUITE GOOD. FUNNY. NICE VOICE TOO.
WHERE DO YOU GET TIME FOR MUSICAL APPRECIATION, PENDER? CONTROL NOT WORKING YOU HARD ENOUGH?
HOW'S IT LOOK?
TOUCH AND GO.
IF HE DOES MAKE IT, HE WON'T BE SINGING AGAIN.
"THEY SHOT HIS THROAT OUT."
DO YOUR BEST. CHANCES ARE HE STUMBLED UPON THE AMBUSH, WITNESSED EVERYTHING. THAT'S WHY THEY SHOT HIM.
KEEP ME INFORMED, PENDER. I WANT THESE CREEPS.
I'LL GIVE 'EM TOTAL WAR!

THE CITY'S JUMPING. CRIME RUNNING OUT OF CONTROL.
SAME OLD SONG.
NO TIME TO STOP, NO TIME TO THINK—
BREAK 'EM UP!
RUN 'EM IN!
TAKE 'EM OUT!
BLOW 'EM DOWN!
BAG 'EM UP!
CART 'EM OFF!
JUSTICE.
SET IT TO THE TUNE OF "RAWHIDE."
THAT'S THE SONG OF THE JUDGES.
TUNE IN— OR DROP OUT.
ROT GUT
THE TREMBLING TASH
NO

JUST TELL US WHAT YOU SAW, CITIZEN.
TAP TAP
CAN'T REMEMBER
THEY GOT YOU IN THE THROAT, NOT THE BRAIN. THINK! YOU MUST REMEMBER!
PLEASE, HE'S STILL VERY WEAK.
AND FOUR JUDGES ARE VERY DEAD.
HE NEEDS REST. PERHAPS IN A FEW DAYS.
I'LL DECIDE WHEN HE NEEDS REST!
WHAT AM I ARGUING WITH A ROBOT FOR? GET IT OUTTA HERE, PENDER!
I KNOW YOU'VE BEEN THROUGH A LOT, BEENY... YOU DON'T WANT TO BE BOTHERED WITH ALL THESE QUESTIONS...
BUT THERE'S A GANG OF PSYCHOPATHS OUT THERE WHO SEEM TO THINK IT'S THEIR GRUD-GIVEN RIGHT TO MURDER A JUDGE OR TWO—

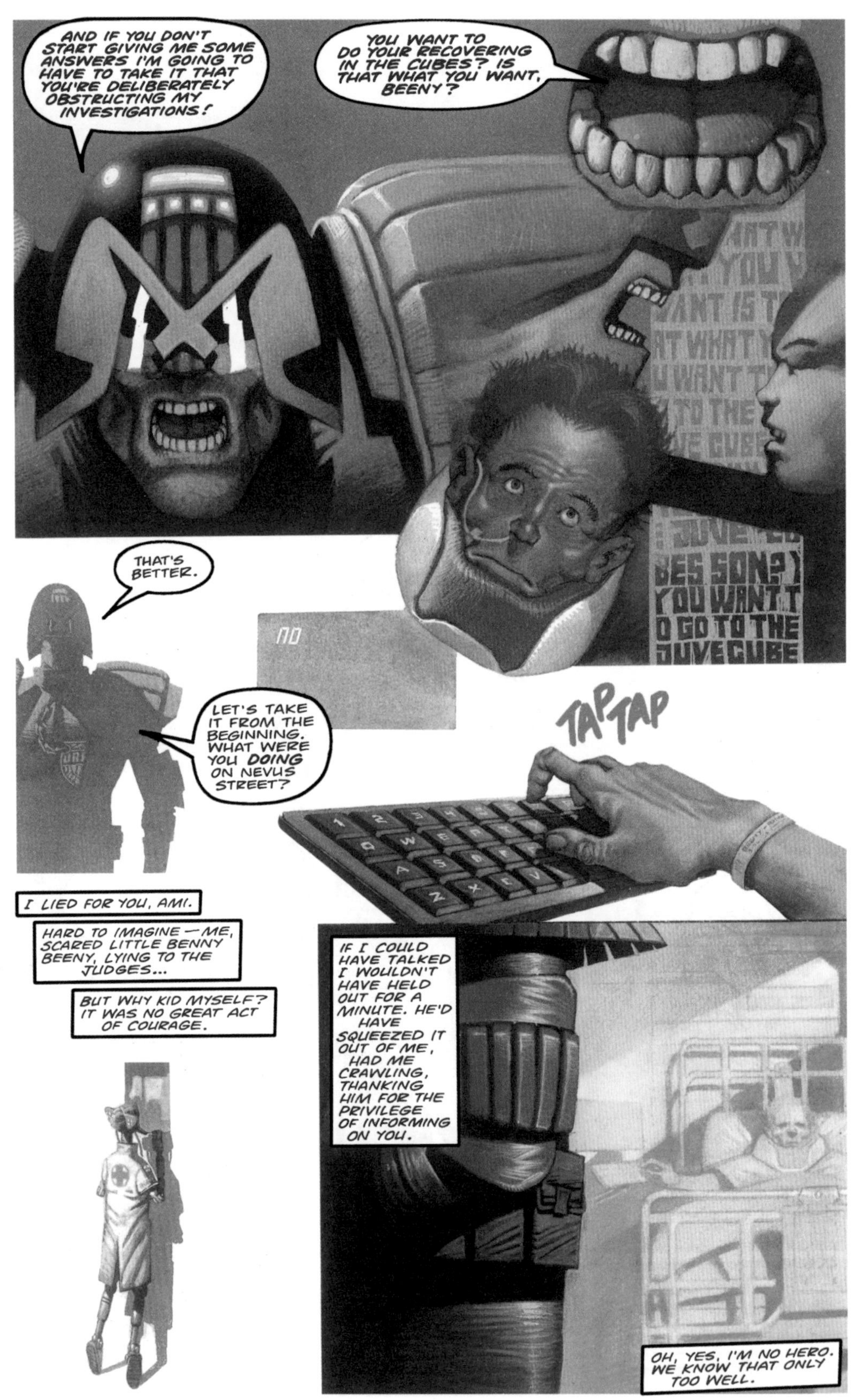

AND IF YOU DON'T START GIVING ME SOME ANSWERS I'M GOING TO HAVE TO TAKE IT THAT YOU'RE DELIBERATELY OBSTRUCTING MY INVESTIGATIONS!
YOU WANT TO DO YOUR RECOVERING IN THE CUBES? IS THAT WHAT YOU WANT, BEENY?
THAT'S BETTER.
NO
LET'S TAKE IT FROM THE BEGINNING. WHAT WERE YOU DOING ON NEVUS STREET?
TAP TAP
I LIED FOR YOU, AMI.
HARD TO IMAGINE — ME, SCARED LITTLE BENNY BEENY, LYING TO THE JUDGES...
BUT WHY KID MYSELF? IT WAS NO GREAT ACT OF COURAGE.
IF I COULD HAVE TALKED I WOULDN'T HAVE HELD OUT FOR A MINUTE. HE'D HAVE SQUEEZED IT OUT OF ME, HAD ME CRAWLING, THANKING HIM FOR THE PRIVILEGE OF INFORMING ON YOU.
OH, YES, I'M NO HERO. WE KNOW THAT ONLY TOO WELL.

THREE MAYBE FOUR
HAPPENED SO FAST CAN'T BE SURE
SHOOTING. JUDGES FALLING. MAN COME AT ME WITH GUN
DONT REMEMBER
BIG LOTS OF MUSCLES TANK TOP UNSHAVEN
NO
CAN'T REMEMBER
IM TRYING

BUT I LEFT MY THROAT ON NEVUS STREET AND HE COULDN'T GET TO ME. SO I LIED. IT WAS DARK, IT ALL HAPPENED SO FAST...

...MY MEMORY SO HAZY, MY HAND DRAGGING SLOWLY OVER THE KEYBOARD, STRETCHING EACH WORD, EACH LETTER INTO AN ETERNITY...

AND JUDGE DREDD IS NOT A PATIENT MAN.

12:07

HE STOPPED ON NEVUS STREET TO LOOK FOR A PUBLIC FACILITY. THE FIRST THING HE NOTICED WAS WHEN THE SHOOTING STARTED. THERE WERE THREE, POSSIBLY FOUR TERRORISTS, HE CAN'T BE SURE.
THE MAN WHO SHOT HIM WAS MUSCULAR, AGE 20-30 APPROXIMATE, UNSHAVEN, TANK TOP. ONE OF THEM WAS A WOMAN—TALL, DARK HAIR, THAT'S ALL HE REMEMBERS. HE WOULDN'T RECOGNISE ANY OF THEM AGAIN.
NOT MUCH HELP, ARE YOU, CITIZEN?
YEAH, I KNOW, YOU'RE SORRY. SO AM I.
THAT'S ALL FOR NOW. YOU REMEMBER ANYTHING ELSE—THE SLIGHTEST DETAIL—I WANT TO KNOW ABOUT IT.
SOR
HE'S RESTING.

WHAT DO YOU THINK?
I THINK ONLY A FOOL STOPS ON NEVUS LOOKING FOR A PF.
HIS SLAX WERE HEAVILY SOILED.
SO WOULD YOURS BE IF YOU'D JUST HAD YOUR THROAT SHOT OUT.

PROBABLY DOESN'T WANT TO ADMIT HE WAS LOOKING FOR A SLABWALKER. WE CAN PULL HIM FOR CONSORTING.
NO, LET IT GO. CREEP'S ALREADY LOST A CAREER ANYWAY.

YOU'RE ALL HEART.

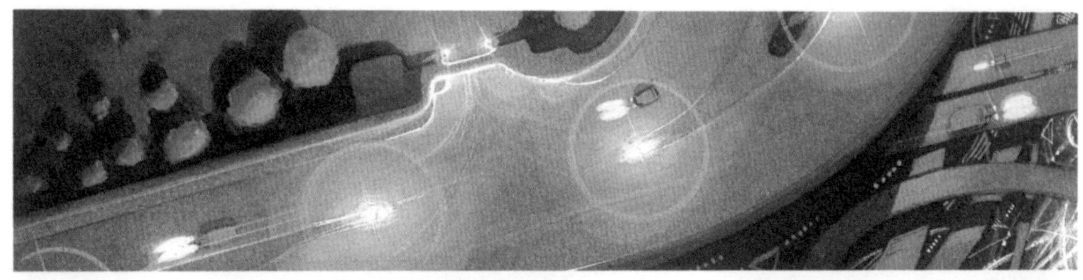

STOP
RIDLEY ESTATE

DELIVERY FOR BEENY.
SECURITY
SECURITY
FIRST RIGHT— THE BIG PLACE ON THE HILL.

BEENY
ROSES

BING BONG!

I'LL GET IT.

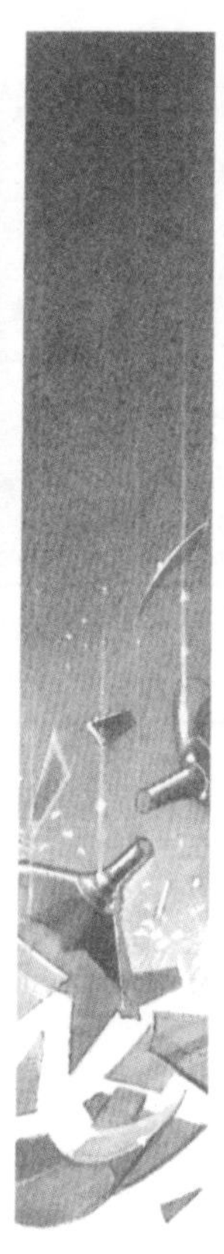

HELLO, BENNY.

CAN I COME IN?
UH...UH... SURE! YEAH!

DON'T WORRY, I WASN'T FOLLOWED.
THEY COULD BE WATCHING THE HOUSE—

NOBODY WAS WATCHING. TAKE MY WORD. I'M GOOD AT THESE THINGS.

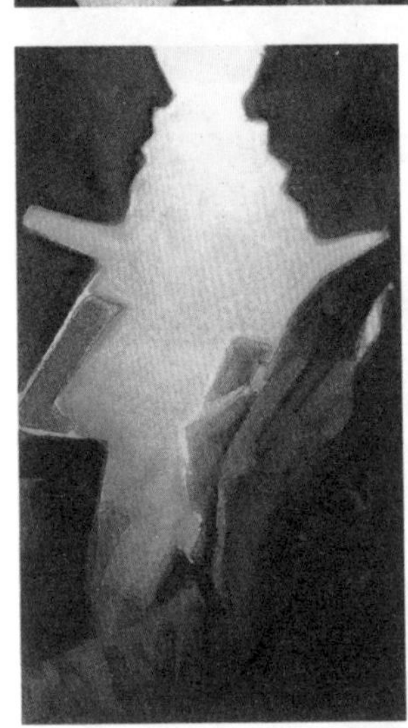

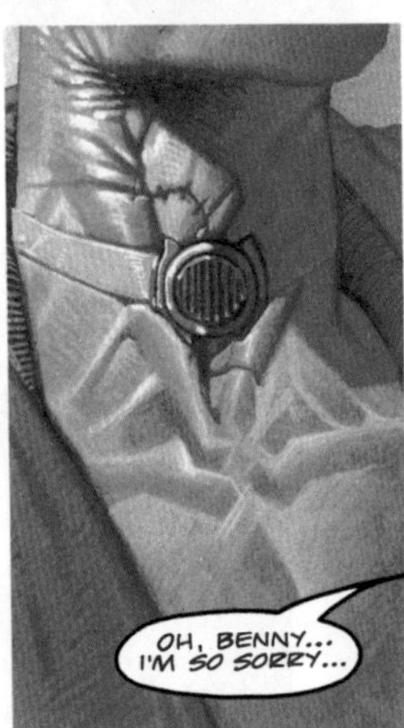
OH, BENNY... I'M SO SORRY...

I COULD HAVE KILLED KURD FOR WHAT HE DID!
IT'S ALL RIGHT. IT'S ONLY TEMPORARY.

THEY'RE GOING TO FIX ME UP WITH AN IMPLANT— PROGRAMMED WITH MY OWN VOICE.
IT'LL NEVER BE QUITE THE SAME, BUT...

IS EVERYTHING ALL RIGHT, SIR?
UH, YEAH, THIS IS, UH, AMERICA, ROBERT—AN OLD FRIEND.

YES, I RECOGNISE THE YOUNG LADY NOW, SIR.
YOU RECOGNISE HER?

YOU KEEP HER HOLOGRAM, SIR. BY YOUR BEDSIDE.

CAN I GET YOU SOMETHING, MIZ? A DRINK?
THAT WOULD BE NICE.
THOUGH IF YOU'LL PARDON ME SAYING SO, A GOOD SQUARE MEAL MIGHT BE MORE IN ORDER.

YOU'VE DONE WELL FOR YOURSELF, BENNY.
YES, EVEN IF I NEVER SING AGAIN MY ACCOUNTANT SAYS I CAN LIVE FAIRLY COMFORTABLY OFF ROYALTIES FOR THE REST OF MY LIFE.
I GUESS YOU'VE PROVED YOUR POINT. I'M GLAD FOR YOU.

I REFRAINED FROM TELLING HER THAT SHE COULD HAVE BEEN PART OF EVERYTHING — COULD STILL BE IF SHE'D WANTED TO. I KNEW IT WAS A WASTE OF TIME.

THANKS — FOR NOT INFORMING ON US. YOU HAD EVERY RIGHT TO, CONSIDERING WHAT HAPPENED.
HOW DO YOU KNOW I DIDN'T?
MY PICTURE WOULD HAVE BEEN ON EVERY NEWSCAST. I WOULDN'T BE HERE NOW — I'D BE DEAD OR IN A CUBE.

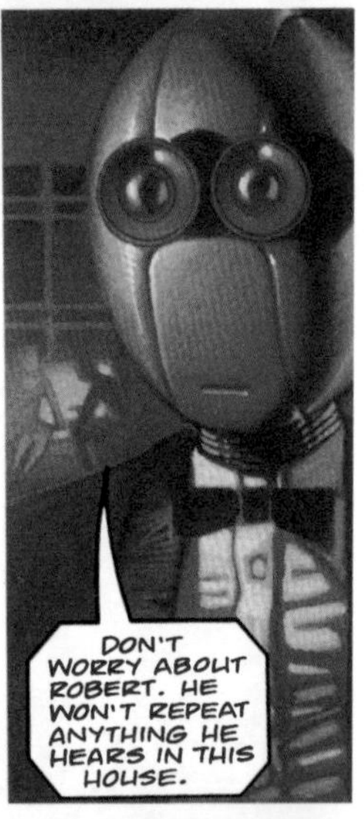

DON'T WORRY ABOUT ROBERT. HE WON'T REPEAT ANYTHING HE HEARS IN THIS HOUSE.

WHAT I DID WAS FOR YOU, AMI, NOT FOR THEM. NOT FOR TOTAL WAR, OR WHATEVER YOU CALL YOURSELVES.
WHAT YOU'RE DOING IS WRONG. KILLING JUDGES — HOW MANY NOW, SIX? — IT'S MURDER, AMI.
NO MATTER HOW YOU DRESS IT UP, IT'S MURDER.

I KNOW...
THEN WHY?

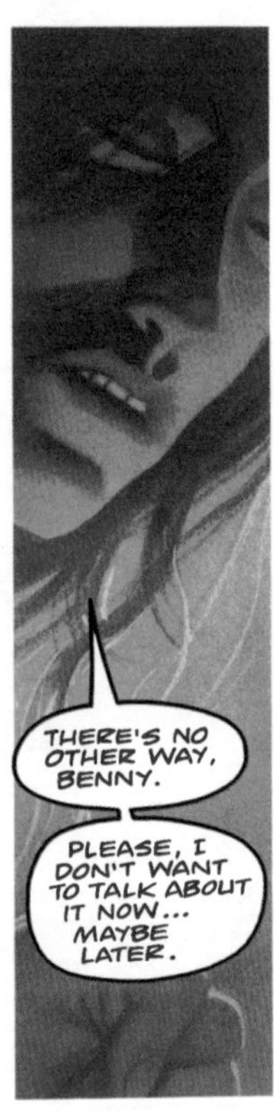

THERE'S NO OTHER WAY, BENNY.
PLEASE, I DON'T WANT TO TALK ABOUT IT NOW... MAYBE LATER.

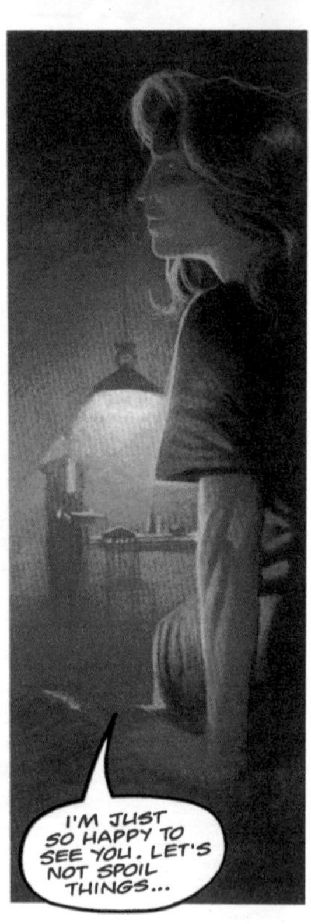

I'M JUST SO HAPPY TO SEE YOU. LET'S NOT SPOIL THINGS...

SHE ATE LIKE SHE HADN'T SEEN REAL FOOD FOR A WEEK. SHE HADN'T BEEN LOOKING AFTER HERSELF.
SHE'D BEEN LIVING ROUGH, MOVING FROM HOUSE TO HOUSE — SYMPATHISERS — NEVER STAYING TOO LONG IN ONE PLACE.

OHHHHHH... STUFFED!
'MEMBER THAT TIME WE GOT HOLD OF MOM'S TAFFEE MIX?

DO I? YOU HAD GUNK ALL UP YOUR NOSE AND IN YOUR HAIR. YOUR TUMMY WAS SO TIGHT YOU COULD HARDLY STAND!
YOU'RE ONE TO TALK! YOU'RE THE ONE WHO WAS UP BEING SICK ALL NIGHT!

WE TALKED LONG INTO THE NIGHT. FOR A FEW HOURS IT WAS JUST LIKE OLD TIMES, AS IF THE REAL WORLD HAD NEVER INTRUDED ON OUR LIVES.

BUT IN THE END THERE WAS NO KEEPING IT OUT...
THE JUDGES WILL GET YOU. YOU KNOW THAT, DON'T YOU? THEY ALWAYS DO.
YES.

WHY DON'T YOU STOP?
I CAN'T.
OF COURSE YOU CAN. YOU'VE NEVER BEEN IDENTIFIED. JUST QUIT—WALK AWAY. I'LL HELP YOU.
I'VE GOT EVERYTHING WE COULD EVER NEED HERE. LIVE WITH ME. WE COULD BE HAPPY TOGETHER, I KNOW IT.

DAMN! I PROMISED MYSELF I WASN'T GOING TO SAY THAT...
OH, HELL. AMI, YOU KNOW HOW I FEEL ABOUT YOU.

YOU DON'T KNOW HOW TEMPTING IT IS...
I'M TIRED... TIRED OF RUNNING, TIRED OF HIDING. BUT THERE'S NO WAY BACK NOW.
THEY HURT ME, BENNY. I CAN'T STOP HATING THEM.
WE'LL TALK MORE ABOUT IT IN THE MORNING. I'LL HAVE ROBERT MAKE YOU UP A BED.
THERE'S NO NEED FOR THAT.
YOU CAN'T LEAVE NOW. IT'S AFTER THREE.
THAT'S NOT WHAT I MEANT, DUMMY.
YOU M-MEAN—?
I... I CAN'T
NOT LIKE THIS.
DON'T BE SILLY.
COME ON.
GRUD, YOU HAVEN'T CHANGED, HAVE YOU?
YOU'RE A REALLY NICE GUY, BENNY, BUT YOU'RE SUCH A JERK.

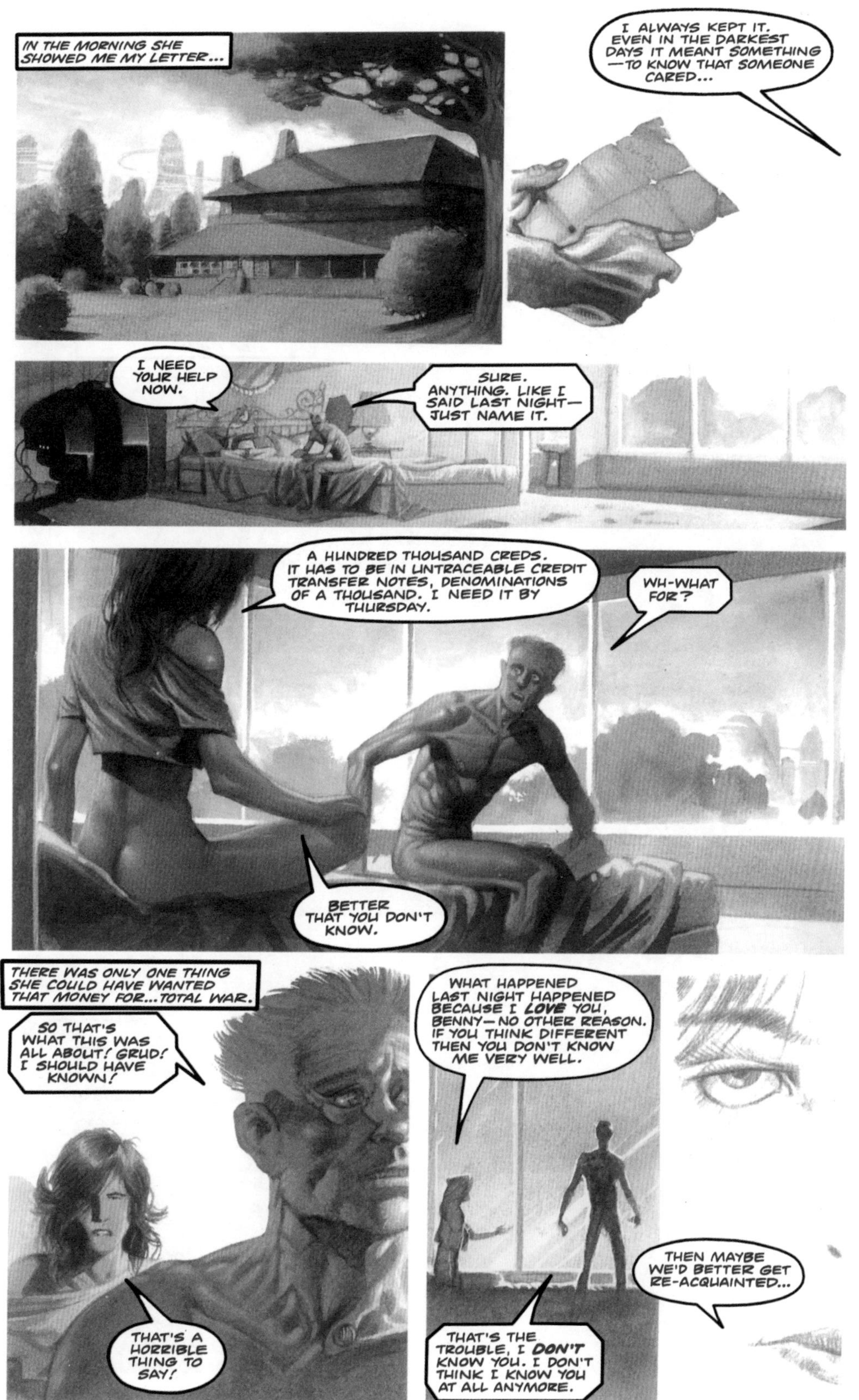
IN THE MORNING SHE SHOWED ME MY LETTER...
I ALWAYS KEPT IT. EVEN IN THE DARKEST DAYS IT MEANT SOMETHING —TO KNOW THAT SOMEONE CARED...
I NEED YOUR HELP NOW.
SURE. ANYTHING. LIKE I SAID LAST NIGHT— JUST NAME IT.
A HUNDRED THOUSAND CREDS. IT HAS TO BE IN UNTRACEABLE CREDIT TRANSFER NOTES, DENOMINATIONS OF A THOUSAND. I NEED IT BY THURSDAY.
WH-WHAT FOR?
BETTER THAT YOU DON'T KNOW.
THERE WAS ONLY ONE THING SHE COULD HAVE WANTED THAT MONEY FOR...TOTAL WAR.
SO THAT'S WHAT THIS WAS ALL ABOUT! GRUD! I SHOULD HAVE KNOWN!
THAT'S A HORRIBLE THING TO SAY!
WHAT HAPPENED LAST NIGHT HAPPENED BECAUSE I LOVE YOU, BENNY—NO OTHER REASON. IF YOU THINK DIFFERENT THEN YOU DON'T KNOW ME VERY WELL.
THAT'S THE TROUBLE, I DON'T KNOW YOU. I DON'T THINK I KNOW YOU AT ALL ANYMORE.
THEN MAYBE WE'D BETTER GET RE-ACQUAINTED...

SHE TOLD ME SHE'D BEEN ON THE BIG DEMOCRATIC MARCH, HER AND DOOD. SHE WAS FOUR MONTHS PREGNANT.
THEY WERE SIXTEEN MILLION STRONG, MARCHING ON THE GRAND HALL—A HUGE TIDAL WAVE OF PEACEFUL PROTEST. THEY FELT NOTHING COULD STOP THEM.
PEOPLE
THEN THE STONE THROWING STARTED... JUSTICE DEPARTMENT AGITATORS, PLANTED IN THE MARCH.
COME ON, HOW CAN YOU SAY THAT?
I KNOW. IT'S THE WAY THEY WORK.
IT GAVE THE JUDGES ALL THE EXCUSE THEY NEEDED--
FREEDOM
NO VIOLENCE! NO VIOLENCE!
DOOD!
LEAVE HIM ALONE—!

DOOD DIED ON THE WAY TO HOSPITAL— BRAIN HAEMORRHAGE. I NEARLY LOST THE BABY.
I WAS SENT TO A REHAB UNIT FOR "RE-EDUCATION," AS THEY CALLED IT.
HE WAS A LITTLE BOY, YOU KNOW... WE WERE GOING TO CALL HIM TONY, AFTER MY DAD.
I'D BEEN IN REHAB TWO MONTHS WHEN THEY CAME FOR HIM...
GENETIC ABNORMALITY, I'M AFRAID. ROUTINE AMNIOCENTESIS PICKED IT UP.
THERE'S NOTHING TO BE ASHAMED OF. IT HAPPENS.
JUST COME WITH US.
WHAT—? N-NO! YOU CAN'T DO THIS!
NOT MY BABY—!
I... DIDN'T KNOW. I'M SORRY...
THEY DID IT DELIBERATELY!
SURELY NOT—
OH YES! YOU DON'T KNOW THEM!
AND EVEN IF THEY DIDN'T WHAT RIGHT HAVE THEY GOT TO MURDER MY BABY? WHAT RIGHT HAVE THEY GOT TO DECIDE WHO LIVES AND WHO DIES?

I ENDED UP IN THE PSYCHO CUBES, MUCH OF THE TIME UNDER RESTRAINT. CLASSIFIED HOSTILE.
BUT IT GAVE ME TIME TO THINK. GRADUALLY I BEGAN TO CALM DOWN, PLAY ALONG WITH THEM. I KNEW I HAD TO GET OUT OF THERE—
—TO FIGHT THEM, BENNY!
IT WASN'T HARD TO FIND OTHERS WHO FELT THE SAME WAY. THE DEMOCRATIC MARCH HAD CHANGED A LOT OF PEOPLE.
MAYBE THERE IS ANOTHER WAY. MAYBE ONE DAY PEACEFUL PROTEST WILL WIN. BUT I JUST DON'T CARE ANYMORE.
OH, AMERICA. WERE YOU USING ME EVEN THEN? YOU KNEW JUST THE RIGHT WORDS TO TWIST ME WITH—NEVER SEE YOU AGAIN...
NO! I WON'T BELIEVE IT OF HER!
I PROMISE YOU NO ONE WILL BE HURT BY THIS MONEY. IF YOU DON'T WANT TO DO IT, I'LL UNDERSTAND.
I WON'T GET YOU INVOLVED. IF YOU SAY NO I'LL WALK OUT OF HERE AND YOU'LL NEVER SEE ME AGAIN.
N-NO...
THURSDAY, YOU SAID...?

WE ARRANGED TO MEET AT A NORTH SECTOR HOV-IN. IT WAS SAFER, SHE SAID, IF SHE DIDN'T COME TO THE HOUSE AGAIN.
HOV-IN

NO
OVER

WE SAT FOR A WHILE, GENTLY SWINGING, WATCHING THE ACTORS MOUTH THEIR SOUNDLESS WORDS. SHE HELD MY HAND. I FELT A STRANGE SENSE OF CONTENTMENT.

IF ONLY IT COULD HAVE STAYED LIKE THAT— IF WE COULD HAVE WALKED AWAY, TOGETHER, TURNED OUR BACKS ON THE TRAGEDY THAT HAD BEEN SO CAREFULLY LAID OUT BEFORE US.
BUT LIFE DOESN'T WORK THAT WAY.
DID YOU BRING THE MONEY?

WHAT ARE YOU GOING TO DO WITH THIS?
I TOLD YOU, BETTER YOU DON'T KNOW.
I'VE GOT TO KNOW, AMI. I... HAVE TO BE SURE NO ONE'S GOING TO BE HURT. I CAN'T GIVE IT TO YOU UNLESS YOU TELL ME.

IT'S TO BUY EXPLOSIVES.
WE'RE GOING TO BLOW UP THE STATUE OF LIBERTY.

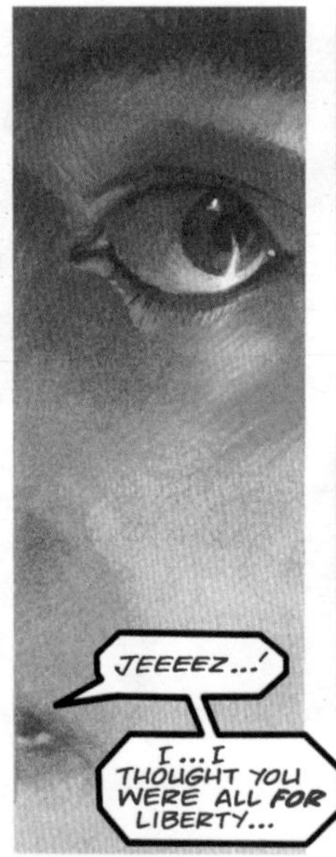
JEEEEZ...!
I... I THOUGHT YOU WERE ALL FOR LIBERTY...

THERE'S NO LIBERTY, NOT HERE. THE STATUE'S A SICK JOKE.
WE'RE JUST MAKING A POINT. HEADLINES— THAT'S WHAT IT'S ALL ABOUT, ISN'T IT? SOONER OR LATER THE MESSAGE WILL GET THROUGH.

I WORMED IT ALL OUT OF HER— DATE, TIME AND M.O. THERE'D BE TWO HOVER PODS, ONE PACKED WITH EXPLOSIVE ON A TWENTY MINUTE SWITCH, TO GIVE THEM TIME TO GET CLEAR AND GIVE A WARNING.
THANK YOU.
AMERICA WOULD BE DRIVING THE ESCAPE POD.

AFTERWARDS... YOU'LL GIVE THIS UP, WON'T YOU?
I'LL THINK ABOUT IT, BENNY.

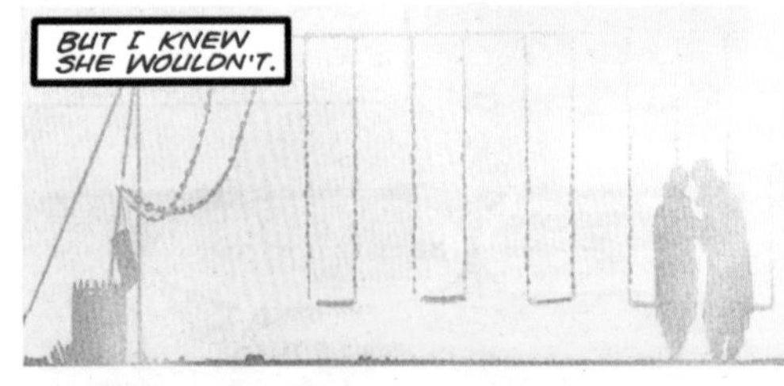
BUT I KNEW SHE WOULDN'T.

NO JUVES OVER 12

I DON'T WANT TO LOSE YOU AGAIN, AMI...
DINER
EXIT

SHE JUST LOOKED AT ME—AS IF SHE KNEW.

OBSERVATION UNITS REPORT SUSPICIOUS POD HOVERING APPROXIMATELY ONE HALF KAY SOUTH. POD REGISTERED TO ONE BEENY, BENNETT.
YOU WANT A PICK UP?
NEGATIVE. LET HIM WATCH.

HE EARNED IT.

SIGHTING! ONE KAY WEST OVER DEETER SKED AND CLOSING!
ROJ. WE HAVE THEM ON VISUAL.
DISRUPTERS.
CHECK!
WE'RE LOSING POWER—!
KURD'S GOING DOWN TOO! SOMETHING'S UP!
SWEET MOTHER—!

IT'S A SET UP!
LIBERTY BAY

THAT DAMNED FRIEND OF YOURS!
BENNY? NO! BENNY WOULDN'T DO THAT!

NO CONTEST! NO CONTEST!

FIRE AT WILL.

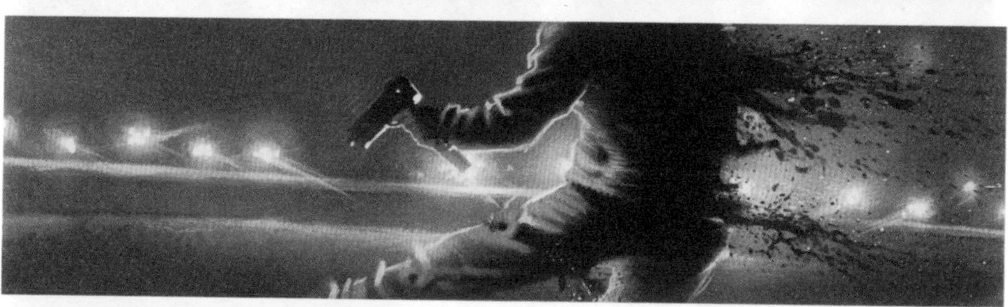

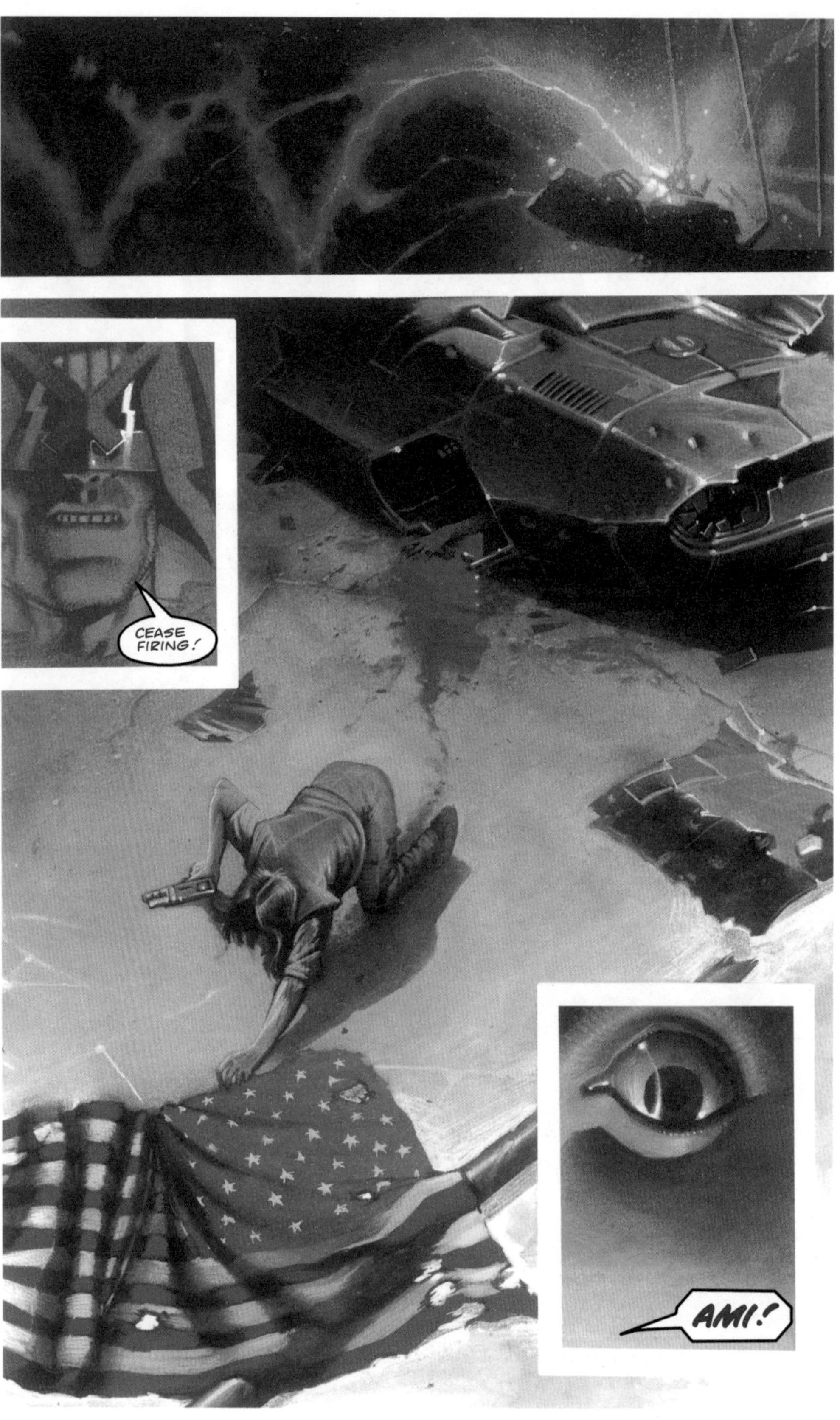
CEASE FIRING!
AMI!

YES, I REMEMBER AMERICA...

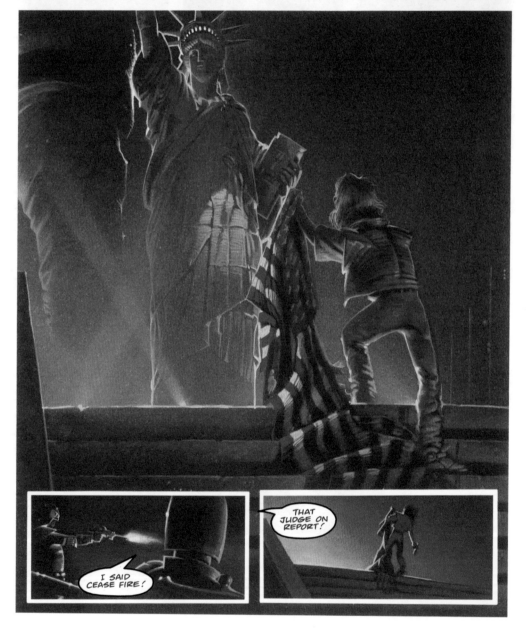

STRUGGLING TO RISE—

— TAKING THOSE LAST, FALTERING STEPS ACROSS THE CONCOURSE.

I SAID CEASE FIRE!

THAT JUDGE ON REPORT!

AMI!

LEAVE HIM!
IT'S OUR INFORMER.

OH, JESUS, AMI, DON'T DIE! PLEASE, DON'T DIE!

MEDIC! GET A MEDIC!

I'M SO SORRY! I HAD TO TELL THEM! I-IF I'D JUST GIVEN YOU THE MONEY I'D HAVE BEEN INVOLVED IN MURDER—TERRORISM! I-I COULDN'T DO IT, AMI—!

START ROUNDING UP SYMPATHISERS—THE WHOLE RING.
WHAT ABOUT BEENY? HE'S GUILTY OF CONCEALING EVIDENCE.
HE'S BEEN VERY CO-OPERATIVE. WE'LL LET THIS ONE GO.

IT-IT WAS FOR THE BEST, AMI! HE SAID YOU WOULDN'T BE HURT—JUST THE OTHERS!
MEDIC!

YOU SAID YOU WOULDN'T HURT HER!
SPARE YOUR TEARS FOR SOMEONE WHO DESERVES THEM, BEENY. SHE WAS A JUDGE KILLER.
BUT YOU FOLLOWED HER FROM THE HOV-IN! YOU KNEW THEM ALL! YOU COULD HAVE PICKED THEM UP ANY TIME! WHY THIS?
A LITTLE DEMONSTRATION— TO ENCOURAGE THE OTHERS.
YOU'RE NOT THE ONLY ONE IN SHOW BUSINESS.
DAMN YOU!
DAMN YOU...!

Tonite
BENNETT BEENY
in CABARET
LADIES AND GENTLEMEN, THOSE OF YOU WITH MEMORIES STRETCHING BACK OVER A YEAR—
OKAY, I REALISE IT AIN'T MANY, BUT THERE MUST BE A **FEW** IN TONIGHT!

SOME OF YOU DIMWITS MAY VAGUELY REMEMBER THE TRAGIC SHOOTING THAT STRUCK DOWN ONE OF THIS CITY'S WITTIEST, WACKIEST TALENTS.
THAT NIGHT THEY SAID HE WOULD NEVER SING AGAIN. WE AT JERALDO'S **TALK OF THE MEG** ARE PROUD THAT HE IS HERE TONIGHT TO PROVE THEM WRONG—
—MAYBE A LITTLE **DIFFERENT** FROM WHAT YOU REMEMBER, BUT STILL EVERY INCH A STAR.

SO WON'T YOU PLEASE PUT YOUR MITTS TOGETHER TO WELCOME BACK--

FIRE
BENNNETTTT **BEENY!**

JEEEZ, IT'S **TRUE!** FULL-BODY TRANSPLANT!
BUT CAN SHE **SING?**

A LUMP OF THE GETAWAY VEHICLE WAS LODGED IN AMI'S SKULL. SHE WAS DECLARED BRAIN DEAD BEFORE SHE REACHED HOSPITAL.

WE NEED TO KNOW NEXT OF KIN.
ST. MAGNUS PIK
ST MA
MEM
HOSP.

NOBODY... THERE'S NOBODY. ONLY ME.
AND YOU ARE?

I WAS... HER FRIEND.
AND THE WORD STUCK IN MY THROAT.

THE OTHER INJURIES CAN BE REPAIRED, BUT... FRANKLY, THE KINDEST THING IS TO SWITCH OFF.
NO! DON'T DO THAT!

I HAD AMI MADE OVER TO MY CUSTODY. WHEN YOU'RE RICH ENOUGH, ALMOST ANYTHING CAN BE ARRANGED.
TALK OF MEG
I KEPT HER ON LIFE SUPPORT FOR THREE MONTHS BEFORE I MADE THE DECISION.

MUSCLE CO-ORDINATION IS STILL TRICKY AND MY FINGERS ARE TOO CLUMSY TO MANAGE THE GITTER, BUT I'M SLOWLY GETTING USED TO IT.

WHY DID I DO IT? I'M STILL NOT SURE MYSELF.
BAR
I KNOW THAT PART OF ME COULD NEVER TAKE THAT FINAL STEP— NEVER BRING MYSELF TO SWITCH OFF AND END HER LIFE FOREVER.

I'M NOT HERE TO SING ANY FUNNY LITTLE NUMBERS.
YOU CAN LAUGH ABOUT THINGS FOR ONLY SO LONG.

AND I KNOW THAT I DID IT TO PUNISH MYSELF. BECAUSE NOT A DAY PASSES WHEN I DON'T SEE HER FACE IN THE MIRROR AND REMEMBER WHAT I DID.
SHE'S ALL AROUND ME, EVERY MOMENT— THE TOUCH, THE SMELL OF HER.
I HAD A FRIEND. HER NAME WAS AMERICA.
THIS IS HER SONG.

BUT I LIKE TO THINK THAT I DID IT FOR AMI, TOO. SO THAT AT LEAST PART OF HER — AT LEAST HER **DREAM** COULD CARRY ON.
BECAUSE SHE WAS RIGHT. YOU CAN'T IGNORE WHAT'S GOING ON. YOU CAN'T BURY YOUR HEAD IN THE SAND AND FORGET WHAT THE JUDGES ARE DOING TO US.
YOU'VE GOT TO KEEP FIGHTING.
NOW IS THE TIME
DEM
YOU'VE GOT TO KEEP LOOKING FOR AMERICA.
TOTAL
Dear Ami,
Now mom's gone there's no reason for me to hang around old Fred Neitzsche. So I guess this is goodbye. I don't think I'll write any more. I'm sure you understand.
I just want you to know that I'll always love you. If you ever need me, I'm there.
Take care of yourself
Benny

FREEDOM — POWER TO THE PEOPLE — DEMOCRACY... THE GREAT AMERICAN DREAM.
DON'T KID YOURSELF.
WE TRIED IT BEFORE. BELIEVE ME, IT DOESN'T WORK. YOU CAN'T TRUST THE PEOPLE.
SO DREAM ON, CREEP. BUT JUST REMEMBER — THAT'S ALL IT IS, A DREAM...
AMERICA IS DEAD.
THIS IS THE REAL WORLD.
MACNEIL '90

2312 HOURS. JUDGE DREDD IS ON PATROL.
THAT'S FREEZ McCANN, ONE OF CUBEMAN'S GORILLAS. WHAT'S HE UP TO?
WELL, WELL, THE BIG CUBE HIMSELF.
THE SHIP LEAVES AT MIDNIGHT, BOSS — STRAIGHT RUN TO PROXIMA 4. THE GUARD AT THE SPACE-PORT'S BEEN PAID TO LOOK THE OTHER WAY.
THEN I'LL BE OUTA THIS STINKIN' CITY FOR GOOD!
'MR CUBE' KNOWS IF ANYTHING GOES WRONG THE JUDGES ARE GOING TO PUT HIM IN A CUBE FOR THE REST OF HIS UNNATURAL LIFE.
UH-OH, LOOKS LIKE WE PICKED UP A TAIL.
FUGITIVE CARL CUBEMAN — AKA MR CUBE — PASSENGER IN BLACK JAGSTER HEADING SOUTH ON PLATH! AM IN PURSUIT!

2313 HOURS. THE ROBO-SERVANTS' IMPROVEMENT GROUP LEAVES A MEETING HALL BENEATH THE SOUTHBOUND SKED.
AN EXCELLENT TALK I THOUGHT. LESSONS WE CAN ALL TAKE TO HEART.
AH, OUR TRANSPORT'S HERE.
ON HIRE
ASH
MYRON
HAL
EX
GOOD MEETING, YOU DROIDS?
HOW COULD ANY MEETING COMPARE WITH THE MEETING OF MY HUMBLE OCULARS AND YOUR HANDSOME FEATURES, GOOD DRIVER? TRULY, YOU ARE PERFECTION IN HUMAN FORM.
UH, RIGHT.
MYR
LECTURE TONIGHT :
PROMOTING BETTER UNDERSTANDING OF OUR HUMAN MASTERS : LECTURE BY SIDNEY 4X
FLATTERY WILL GET YOU EVERYWHERE
I THINK YOU'RE OVERDOING IT A BIT, MYRON.
2314 HOURS. IT'S BEEN A QUIET NIGHT IN THE QUITE NICE BAR.
MIGHT AS WELL CLOSE UP NOW, CHUCK.
QUITE NICE BAR
MRS GUNDERSON'S ASLEEP AGAIN.
POOR OLD DEAR. WAKE HER GENTLY, CHUCK.
YOU BET, MR QUITE.
BRIT-CIT WARM ALE
TEXAS EXPORT

MRS GUNDERSON.
EH? EH?
WE'RE CLOSING UP NOW, MRS GUNDERSON.
OH, I-IT'S YOU, MR QUITE. YOU GAVE ME QUITE A START.
NO, IT'S CHUCK, MRS G — CHUCK! YOU FELL ASLEEP AGAIN.
MY TEETH?
NO, I'VE GOT THEM IN. THEY MUST BE SOMEONE ELSE'S
I'M JUST TRYING TO TELL YOU WE'RE CLOSING UP NOW. YOU'RE THE LAST CUSTOMER.
IT'S VERY KIND OF YOU TO OFFER, BUT I WON'T, THANK YOU. I REALLY MUST BE OFF.
GOODNESS ME, IS THAT THE TIME? I'LL MISS MY LAST BUS.
GOODNIGHT, MR QUITE. SAY GOODNIGHT TO THAT NICE POLITE BOY OF YOURS.
I WILL, MRS GUNDERSON. LET ME HELP YOU UP THE STAIRS.
2316 HOURS.
DROKK!
ON HIRE
SKRIEEEEEEEE
UNNNH!
SKRASHHH
BDAM
WE LOST HIM!
AHHHH!

SKIDDD
KRANGG
FREEZ!
TOO LATE FOR HM! LET'S MOVE! WE CAN STILL MAKE THAT SHIP!
YOU'VE FITTED IN VERY WELL HERE, CHUCK, VERY WELL. YOU'RE GOOD WITH THE CUSTOMERS. I LIKE THAT. I LIKE **YOU**, CHUCK.
THANK YOU, MR QUITE.
I'VE COME TO THINK OF YOU... A BIT LIKE THE **SON** I NEVER HAD.
IN FACT, I WONDER, CHUCK, IF YOU'D CONSIDER LETTING ME **ADOPT** YOU?
I... I... DON'T KNOW QUITE WHAT TO SAY, MR QUITE. I... I'M NOT SURE IF MY MOM AND DAD WOULD LIKE IT...
YES, YES. OF COURSE. SILLY OF ME. FORGET I EVER MENTIONED IT.
NO, I'M FLATTERED, REALLY I AM. I'M **HONOURED** YOU SHOULD ASK. LOOK, I'LL ASK THEM HOW THEY FEEL. I'D SURE LOVE TO HAVE YOU AS A DAD.
YOU DO THAT.
OIDE
IPA
ALCO FLOPS
Mega-Ci PRIDE
OH, LOOK. MRS GUNDERSON'S **ELDSTER CARD.**
MEGA-CITY ELDSTER TREAT HOLDER WITH RESPECT
PLEASE RETURN SYLVIA GUNDER
BETTER GO AFTER HER, CHUCK.

2317 HOURS.
THANK YOU, DRIVER. BRILLIANTLY DRIVEN!
NIGHT, MYRON. SEE YOU NEXT MEETING.
HOLD IT!
ON HIRE
YOU CAN'T COME ON HERE. THIS ISN'T A SCHEDULED SERVICE.
SHUT UP AND DRIVE!
WHAT THE DEVIL HAVE WE GOT HERE—?
HAL
YOU CAN PUT FREEZ McCANN ON ICE! CUBE AND ACCOMPLICE HAVE ABANDONED VEHICLE!
2318 HOURS.
MRS GUNDERSON!
GLAD I CAUGHT YOU. YOU LEFT YOUR ELDSTER CARD.
WH-WHAT? WH-WHO ARE YOU?
IT'S CHUCK, MRS GUNDERSON!

MRS GUNDERSON, THIS ISN'T THE BUS STOP. THIS IS A FIRE HYDRANT. THE BUS STOP IS OVER THERE.
I'M NOT GOING ANYWHERE WITH YOU, YOUNG MAN.
I-I DON'T HAVE MUCH MONEY. Y-YOU CAN HAVE MY ELDSTER CARD--
THIS IS YOUR ELDSTER CARD! IT'S CHUCK, MRS GUNDERSON! I'M TRYING TO HELP YOU. THIS ISN'T A BUS STOP. YOU CAN WAIT HERE ALL NIGHT AND A BUS WON'T COME.
SCREEEEK
WHAKK
TRY TA RADIO FOR HELP, WOULD YA?
TAKE OVER, DIP!
GET US OUTA HERE!
SINGLE TO SYLVIA PLATH, PLEASE.
HU-UHH?
M-MRS GUNDERSON!

2320 HOURS. MRS GUNDERSON, A REGULAR AT THE QUITE NICE BAR, HAS GOT ON THE WRONG BUS. THIS ONE HAS BEEN HIJACKED BY FUGITIVE GANG BOSS CARL CUBEMAN—AKA 'MR CUBE'.
ELV
I'M GLAD YOU CAME ALONG. THERE WAS A VERY STRANGE MAN OUT THERE—I THINK HE WAS TRYING TO MUG ME.
NOW WHERE'S MY ELDSTER CARD...?
I DON'T WANT YOUR FREAKIN' ELDSTER CARD, LADY! GET THE HELL OFF!
WHAT?
I SAID I DON'T WANT NO FREAKIN' ELDSTER CARD!
OH, THAT'S VERY KIND OF YOU. THEY USUALLY ASK, YOU KNOW.
LISTEN, LADY—
STOP ARGUING! JUST DRIVE!
THE OLD BAG COULD BE USEFUL — WE MIGHT NEED A HOSTAGE.
YOU JUST SIT RIGHT DOWN HERE, GRANMA. BEHAVE YOURSELF AND THERE'S A GOOD CHANCE YOU'LL COME OUTA THIS ALIVE.
THANK YOU, YOUNG MAN. YOU WILL BE SURE TO LET ME KNOW WHEN WE GET TO SYLVIA PLATH?
MAY I SAY, SIR, YOUR HANDLING OF THIS HIJACK SITUATION HAS BEEN EXEMPLARY.
THAT A FACT?
INDEED. I THINK I SPEAK FOR MY FELLOW MEMBERS OF THE ROBOT IMPROVEMENT GROUP WHEN I SAY IT IS QUITE OBVIOUS WE'RE IN THE PRESENCE OF A CRIMINAL GENIUS.
LOST IN ADMIRATON, SIR!
PAUL
HAL
HEAR, HEAR!
ASH
BOY, RIGHT LOADA KOOKS WE GOT ON THIS BUS!

2323 HOURS.
JUDGE!
G-GUY WITH A C-CUBE HEAD! HE HAD A GUN! M-M-MRS GUNDERSON GOT ON—!
ON WHAT?
G...G...GREEN LINE HIRE BUS— F-FULL OF ROBOTS!
CITIZEN REQUIRES MEDICAL ATTENTION, KAFKA BOULEVARD! FUGITIVE CARL CUBEMAN NOW ON GREEN LINE BUS, LAST SEEN HEADING SOUTH TOWARDS THE INTERSKED!
WE-WE'RE GOING AWFULLY FAST!
I-I DON'T LIKE TO ASK, BUT THIS SEEMS AN AWFULLY LONG WAY. ARE YOU SURE WE'RE NOT AT SYLVIA PLATH YET?
DON'T WORRY, GRANMA. WE GET ANYWHERE NEAR PLATH YOU'LL BE THE FIRST TO KNOW.
EH?
YOU'LL HAVE TO SPEAK UP. I'M A LITTLE DEAF.
DEAR ME, THESE GLASSES. I'LL HAVE TO GET THEM FIXED. THEY MAKE YOUR HEAD SEEM A VERY STRANGE SHAPE.
PICKED UP ANOTHER TAIL, BOSS!

KREIG! I GOT YOUR SUSPECT GREEN LINE ON THE INTERSKED! CREEPS ARE THROWIN' DROIDS AT ME!
SHRAAAK!
PAUL
KRUNGGG
MUCH AS I ADMIRE YOUR INVENTIVENESS, SIR, YOU DID PROMISE WE WOULD COME TO NO HARM.
CHANGE OF PLAN! DO AS YOU'RE TOLD OR THE OLD BAG DIES!
HAL
I CANNOT ALLOW A HUMAN TO COME TO HARM! A MASTERFUL PLOY, SIR— MASTERFUL!
URNNH!
APOLOGIES!
SKRIIIIEEEEE
THWUMPP

2329 HOURS.
HOW BAD YOU HURT, KREIG?
I'LL LIVE. I'VE CALLED FOR ASISTANCE.
YOU'VE BEEN EXTREMELY BRAVE, SIR! YOU'RE AN EXAMPLE TO US ALL!
SHUT UP! THEY WERE HEADED SOUTH!
YOU CAN'T BRING THAT IN HERE!
YOU BEEN PAID TO LOOK THE OTHER WAY – LOOK THE OTHER WAY!
WHAT'S HAPPENING? IS THIS MY STOP?
HELLO? CONDUCTOR – ARE YOU THERE?
OH DEAR!
NO PROBLEM RECOGNISIN' YOU, HUH, MR CUBE?
WE NEARLY DIDN'T MAKE IT! GET THIS BIRD IN THE AIR NOW IF YOU KNOW WHAT'S GOOD FOR YOU!

2335 HOURS — AND NO REPORT OF THE FUGITIVE VEHICLE —
SOMEBODY SHOULD HAVE SPOTTED IT. MUST HAVE GONE TO GROUND...
THE SPACEPORT... I WONDER. IT FITS. THE ONLY SAFE PLACE FOR CUBEMAN IS OFF PLANET.
I THINK THEY'VE ABANDONED ME. THEY SEEMED SO NICE TOO.
OH DEAR, THIS DOESN'T LOOK LIKE MY BLOCK.
I...I'LL HAVE TO FIND SOMEONE AND ASK THEM — OW!
OH! I'M GLAD I BUMPED INTO YOU. I SEEM TO BE LOST. I... I WONDER IF YOU COULD DIRECT ME TO SYLVIA PLATH BLOCK?
SHIP INCOMING RUNWAY 5
FLIP
DANGER
PING!
THAT WAY. OH, THANK YOU.
NO, SIR, NO GREEN LINE BUS THROUGH HERE.
CHECK WITH YOUR OTHER GATES.
YES, SIR.

THIS IS INTERSTELLAR FREIGHTER PROXIMA TRADER REQUESTING PERMISSION FOR LIFT OFF.
ROGER, PROXIMA TRADER. YOUR DEPARTURE LOGGED AT 23.40 HOURS.
HEY, MAURIE, WHO OWNS THAT GREEN LINER BEHIND THE CARGO SHED?
UH--
I COULDN'T DO NOTHIN' TO STOP THEM! THEY HAD GUNS!
WHEN YOU'RE IN A HOLE, CREEP, LEARN TO STOP DIGGING!
DID I SAY SOMETHING WRONG, MAURIE?
SPACEPORT CONTROL, THIS IS JUDGE DREDD! STOP THE PROXIMA TRADER!

2341 HOURS. ON BOARD THE SPACEFREIGHTER PROXIMA TRADER, FUGITIVE GANG BOSS CARL CUBEMAN – AKA 'MR CUBE'.
SPACEPORT CONTROL TO PROXIMA TRADER! YOU ARE ORDERED TO ABORT LIFT-OFF! RETURN TO LANDING PAD!
SOMETHING'S GONE WRONG! DON'T DO IT!
SPACEPORT CONTROL, THIS IS PROXIMA TRADER. YOUR SIGNAL IS BREAKING UP. ASSUME ALL IS A-OKAY FOR EXIT FROM MEGA-CITY AIRSPACE.
CREEP'S NOT STOPPING! THEY GET UP INTO HYPERDRIVE AND WE'VE LOST CUBEMAN!
SCRIPT JOHN WAGNER
ART HENRY FLINT
LETTERS TOM FRAME
PROXIMA TRADER, I REPEAT-- ABORT LIFT-OFF AND RETURN TO LANDING PAD!
HOLY GRUD! TH-THERE'S SOMEONE ON RUNWAY 5!
OH. OH, DEAR...
IT'S GETTING VERY WINDY. I WONDER IF THERE'S A STORM COMING...?

MAMMOTH 12, ABORT LANDING! REPEAT — ABORT LANDING!
OH, DEAR.

2343 HOURS. MAKING AN EMERGENCY CLIMB, THE MAMMOTH SHIP VEERS UPWARD INTO THE OUTGOING PROXIMA TRADER –
SKERRRUNGGG
RRIP
SWEET GRUD –!
SKREEEEEE
AAAHHH!

THE DAMAGED SHIP'S AUTOPILOT TAKES AUTOMATIC COMMAND, BRINGING IT TO A MID-AIR HALT.
SPACEPORT CONTROL TO PROXIMA TRADER! COME IN PROXIMA TRADER!
SPACEPORT CONTROL! WE'RE GETTING NO ANSWER FROM PROXIMA TRADER.
CAN YOU OVER-RIDE THE AUTOPILOT, BRING HER DOWN?
NEGATIVE. SHE'LL BE LOCKED ON THAT ALTITUDE UNTIL THE TEKS CAN DO IT MANUALLY.
THEN ACTIVATE THE SHIP'S ANTI-GRAV HOIST.
WHEEOOOOEEEEOOOOO
OH!

2348 HOURS. CARNAGE ON THE COMMAND DECK.
HELP...!
I NEARLY MADE IT, DREDD!
NEARLY DOESN'T COUNT.
0031 HOURS. CARL CUBEMAN IS DISPATCHED.
PATCH HIM UP, THEN LOCK HIM AWAY FOR THE REST OF HIS LIFE!
ANYONE EVER TELL YOU YOU WERE MADE FOR A CUBE?
THE ELDSTER ON THE RUNWAY — WHERE IS SHE?
WE GOT HER UNDER INTERROGATION. WE'LL CRACK HER STORY, DON'T WORRY.
YOU WHAAT?
I'M ASKING YOU ONE LAST TIME — HOW DID YOU GET INTO THE SPACEPORT?
WH-WHAT?
SPACE PORT
SPACE PORT
I SAID HOW DID YOU GET INTO THE SPACEPORT?
N-NO, I DON'T WANT TO GO TO THE SPACEPORT! SOB! I WANT TO GO HOME!
YOU STUPID OLD WOMAN, DO YOU THINK YOU'RE FOOLING US WITH THIS STUPID ACT?
THAT'S ENOUGH!

CLEAR OFF!
WE'LL BREAK HER! JUST GIVE US ANOTHER FIVE —
GET BACK TO YOUR DUTIES! I'M SURE YOU'VE PLENTY OF OTHER HELPLESS OLD WOMEN TO BULLY!
SPACE PORT
PORT
DREDD
MRS GUNDERSON, IT'S ME, JUDGE DREDD.
WH-WH-WHAT?
JUDGE DREDD!
OH, OH, IT'S YOU, JUDGE DREDD.
WHAT'S HAPPENING? WHERE AM I? I... I'M TRYING TO GET HOME.
DON'T YOU WORRY, I'LL SEE YOU GET THERE.
0146 HOURS. TRANSPORT ARRIVES FOR MRS GUNDERSON.
DREDD
YOU'VE HAD QUITE A LITTLE ADVENTURE TONIGHT, HAVEN'T YOU?
I BEG YOUR PARDON?
I SAID, YOU'VE HAD QUITE A LITTLE ADVENTURE!
WHO?
YOU!
ME?
OH, DEAR-- I THINK I MUST HAVE MISSED IT.

A PROBLEM JUVE WHO CAN'T BE BEAT!
PROG 542
3 OCT 87
2000 AD
FEATURING JUDGE DREDD
$1.70 Malaysia
75c Australia
85c New Zealand (Inc. G.S.T.)
88g Mercury
210g Venus
66g Mars
110g Saturn
2g Pluto
429g Neptune
28p
EARTH MONEY
IN ORBIT EVERY MONDAY
HEY, MUM AND DAD—AIN'T JUSTICE GREAT?
JUDGE
JUDGE DREDD
LIAM '87.

Beryer Block
Mr & Mrs F. Swindley
Flat 67R
QUINN
BOINGA
BOINGA

BOINGA! BOINGA!

JUDGE DREDD

SCRIPT WAGNER & GRANT
ART LIAM SHARP
LETTERING T FRAME

THE DOOR WAS TRIPLE-LOCKED FROM THE **INSIDE** WHEN WE GOT HERE. WINDOWS TOO. WE FIGURE THE KILLER MUST'VE GOT IN THROUGH THE LETTERBOX.
VID RAG
FREE PRESS
FREE PRESS

THE **LETTERBOX**...?
CALENDER
VID RAG
DREDD

KAREN
BERGER
THEY GO RIGHT UP ALONG THE **CEILING** – STOP ABRUPTLY OVER THE PERCH.

Plip!
Plip!
Plip!
NOTICE THE NUMBER OF SMALL, CIRCULAR IMPRESSIONS THAT SHOW UP UNDER ULTRAVIOLET...
SUCKER MARKS.
UM BUHDUM BUH...
SKRAAAWKKK!

A PET **VULTURE**?
TAKES ALL TYPES.

THIS THING — IT **HAD** TO BE A ROBOT...
YES. THE POISON USED WAS A **SYNTHETIC**, TZ310 — EASILY-ENOUGH MADE BY **ANYONE** WITH A BASIC KNOWLEDGE OF CHEMISTRY.

"WE FIGURE IT WAS AUDIO-DIRECTIONAL — PROBABLY PROGRAMMED TO HOME ON ITS VICTIMS' **HEARTBEAT** — HENCE THE VULTURE."

BDUM BDUM BDUM

DUM BDUMBDUMBDUM..BD

THE **SMELL** ALERTED THE NEIGHBOURS... VICTIMS HAVE BEEN **DEAD** ABOUT EIGHT TO TEN WEEKS... HARD TO TELL.

THE MAN **DIED** WHERE HE *SLEPT*. THE WOMAN MUST'VE WOKEN UP, **PANICKED**...

"LACERATIONS ON HER FEET SUGGEST SHE **STAMPED** REPEATEDLY ON IT..."
MASH
MASH
MASH

Ptiiing

BDUMBDUMBDUMBDUMBDUMBDUMBDUMBDUMBDUM

UUH-
UHH-
UHH-

BDUMBUDUMBDUMBDUMBD.....THUNK!

Plip Plip
Plip
Plip
FRANK AND RODA SWINDLEY. HE WAS FORTY-ONE, SHE WAS FORTY-FOUR. BOTH UNEMPLOYED. LIVED IN THE BLOCK THREE YEARS.
THE MOTIVE... THEFT
NO, AS FAR AS WE CAN TELL NOTHING WAS TAKEN.
67
WINDLEY
CHINK!
ETT
Plip
Plip
WE'RE LOOKING INTO POSSIBLE ENEMIES — ANYONE WHO MIGHT'VE BORNE A GRUDGE AGAINST THEM, HAD REASON TO WANT THEM DEAD. BUT THEY WERE A POPULAR COUPLE.
SO YOU'VE NO LEADS...?
NOTHING SOLID. BUT REST ASSURED — WHOEVER DID IT, WE'LL FIND THEM. WE ALWAYS DO.
WISH I HAD YOUR CONFIDENCE...

HE'D HAD NOTHING AGAINST THE SWINDLEYS -

HE'D NEVER EVEN MET THEM. THEY'D BEEN CHOSEN AT RANDOM FROM THE BLOCK DIRECTORY. NO WAY THE JUDGES WOULD EVER LINK THEM TO HIM.
PJ! HOW MANY TIMES HAVE I TOLD YOU TO STOP BOUNCING THAT BALL IN THE HOUSE!

BOINGA!

YES, MA.

BUG WAS A SOPHISTICATED DEVICE, BUT NOTHING ANY HALFWAY DECENT ROBOTICS TEK COULDN'T COME UP WITH - AND THERE WERE PLENTY OF THEM IN THIS CITY.
WHO'D EVER SUSPECT A TWELVE-YEAR-OLD JUVE?

HIS NAME IS PJ MAYBE. THIS HAS BEEN HIS FIRST MURDER.

IT IS FAR FROM BEING HIS LAST.
JUST THE START... FOR NOW!
THE BEGINNING...

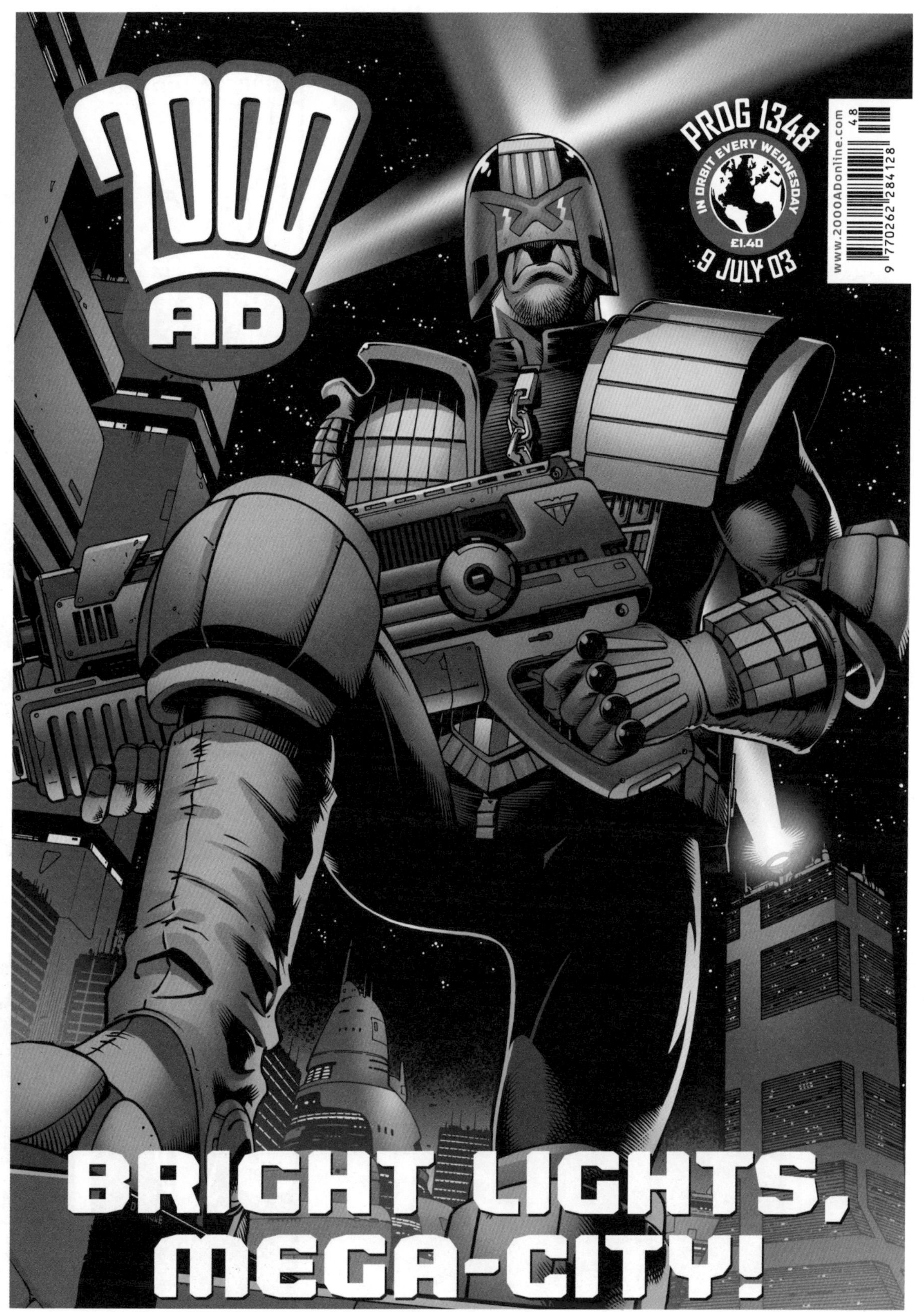
2000 AD
PROG 1348
IN ORBIT EVERY WEDNESDAY
£1.40
9 JULY 03
www.2000ADonline.com
BRIGHT LIGHTS,
MEGA-CITY!

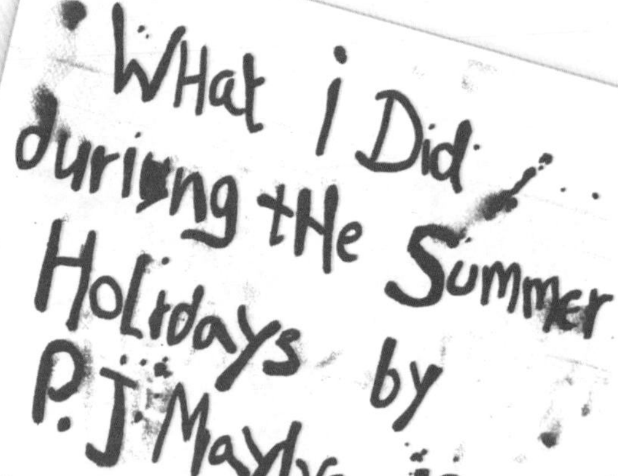

During the summer holiDay Uncle Fustas and cousins Watt and WilBur came round to dinnEr. This was a verY biG ocassion for us because Uncle Fusty is very ricH and Dad works as a trowser designer in his factory. so my Ma took speciaL care over the dinNer, following the directons on the self-heat packs to the leTTer. And we even had shampaign.

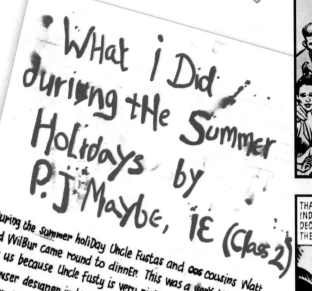

e're the Maybes and theyir the Yesses. Mum used to be a Yess.
ere was a biG storm when she eloped with DaD. They said
e was marrying beNeeth her.

WAS, UH,
UST
CKY, I
JESS...
YOU GUESS! BLISTERING BELLBOTTOMS, MAKE UP YOUR MIND, MAN! EITHER YOU WERE LUCKY OR YOU WEREN'T!

Uncle Fustas owns a biG trowser factory. "Emphatically Yess" Its called. Theyve got the contract To make trowsers for the Judges, which is "Solid Gold", as Uncle Fustas says...

YES SIR! AS LONG AS THERE ARE JUDGES THEY'LL ALWAYS NEED TROUSERS! AND AS LONG AS STREETS ARE HARD THEY'LL ALWAYS NEED MORE! SUPPLY AND DEMAND — MOST BASIC LAW OF BUSINESS!

ler dad. He designed the peepHole pantaloon, wHich was
t spring, and theY still treat him like the cleaning droid.
ts because Jobs are Hard to come by and we need to Keep

AAYBE, THAT IDEA OF YOURS
E-LEG MODEL — HAD TO TURN
IC FLAW IN YOUR ARITHMETIC.
PEOPLE ONLY HAVE TWO.
T'S A
E,
S
I'M DESIGN DIRECTOR, MAYBE — I'LL DECIDE WHAT'S A WINNER. YOU PRODUCE SOME DESIGNS WE CAN SELL OR YOU'LL BE LOOKING FOR ANOTHER POSITION.

While they were talking i excusd myself and went out to tamper with WilBur's car.

I built my ultrasonic Key in teK class. It took me weeks, cos i had to do it in Secret.
WEEEEEEE.
Snick!
I found out a long time ago that its not a good idea to let People know how smart you are – espeshully teachers. They start expecting things of you, want you to do things you don't want to.
Worse, they might suspect you of doing things you'd rather they didnt susspect you of.
BYRO UNIT
THAT MAYBE! HE GETS WORSE AND WORSE! TRYING TO TELL **ME** HOW TO RUN THE DESIGN DEPARTMENT!
WE'VE GOT TO BE FIRM. IF HE'S NOT PULLING HIS WEIGHT I SAY WE AXE HIM.
YES... BUT NOT YET. FOR MARGARET'S SAKE. APART FROM YOU TWO SHE'S THE ONLY FAMILY I'VE GOT.
PITY ABOUT THE MAN. I SUPPOSE IT RUNS IN THE BLOOD. I DID HAVE A MIND TO TAKE YOUNG **P.J.** INTO THE COMPANY, BUT APPARENTLY FROM HIS SCHOOL REPORTS HE'S A BIT OF A DUNCE.
'NIGHT, POP!

LOOK, MARGARET! LOOK AT THESE AND TELL ME I'M WRONG!

WH-WHAT THE HELL-?

TH-THE GYRO!

DAMN! CAN'T CONTROL IT! COME ON, YOU BEGGAR!

CLEAR THE AREA, CITIZENS! MOVE!
OH NO-!

COME ON, YOU B--

VADOOOOM!

AAAGGHHH!

I found out later that seven innocent Bystanders were Killed. Including the Swindleys. that brings the total number of peopel I've murdered to Ten.

I Guess if WilBur knew how danegerous i really am he wouldn't have been so meen to DaD. But that wouldn't have saved him.

Judge Dredd himself came round to break the news. that gave me a real big thrill.

NO–NO! POOR WILBUR!
EITHER OF YOU HAVE ANY KNOWLEDGE OF THIS? EITHER OF YOU GO NEAR MR YESS'S VEHICLE?

GOOD HEAVENS, NO!
YOU-YOU THINK SOMEBODY DID SOMETHING TO IT?
IMPOSSIBLE TO TELL. JUST CHECKING OUT EVERY POSSIBILITY.

I've got to hand it to them. their reactions were real natural – WHICH of corse they ought to have been. anyway, they convinsed old Dredd.
It never ocurred to him to ask the thirteen year old. But then it never does.

THIS IS TERRIBLE! TERRIBLE!
I CAN'T STAND THE GUY BUT I'D NEVER WISH ANYTHING LIKE THIS ON HIM!
I THINK YOU OUGHT TO GO RIGHT OVER AND SEE UNCLE FUSTAS.

TELL HIM HOW SORRY YOU ARE, HOW WILBUR CAN NEVER BE REPLACED...
YES, YOU'RE RIGHT, P.J. POOR MAN! WE'VE GOT TO DO ALL WE CAN TO COMFORT HIM!

Yes, Uncle Fusty was going to need all the comfort we could give him... espeshully when Id got round to disposing of Watt as well!
NEXT PROG: More of What I Did...

What i Did ~~Did~~ During the Summer Holidays

By P.J. Maybe

PART TWO

A week after cousin Wilburs accident i had to attend the funeral. It wasn't a funeral reely – Uncle Fustas had Wilbur stuffed. A mister sardini over on Cassock street made him into a permanent display. Ma said he did a reel good job, very naturel. Mr Sardini must be the best ~~taxid~~ taxydermist in the whole world, cos the accident Report said Wilburd been nearly burnt to a crisp.

so instead of a funeral they held a little ceremoney in mr sardinis' parlour.

WILBUR LIVED FOR HIS JOB. HE DEVOTED HIS LIFE TO MAKING OUR FIRM THE FIRST NAME IN STYLISH LOWER BODY APPAREL...

HE WAS A TRUE **YESS** – A REAL SEAT OF THE PANTS TROUSER MAN!

SOLID GOLD!

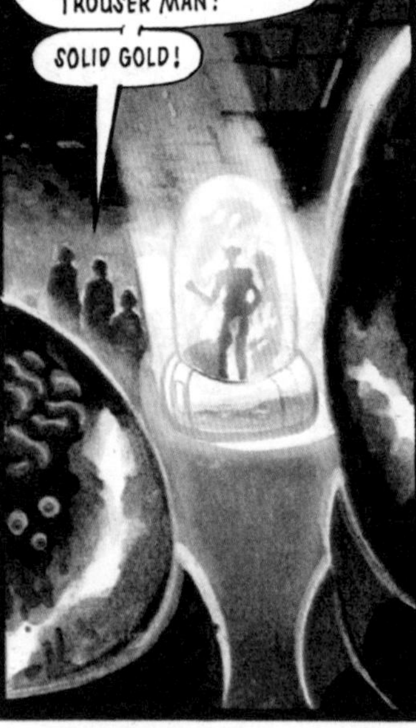

SO IT IS ONLY FITTING THAT HE SHOULD REMAIN A PART OF THIS FIRM, SHARING IN EACH NEW SUCCESS, EACH NEW FASHION FIRST. SO THAT WE MAY RIGHTLY SAY... WILBUR IS NOT DEAD – MERELY MODELLING.

SOB!

Judge Dredd was there as Justice department representive. You could tell he'd rather be out arresting people.

WILBUR YESS WAS A, UH, GOOD CITIZEN AND, UH, A FIRST RATE TROUSER DESIGNER. I DIDN'T KNOW HIM PERSONALLY BUT WE, UH... WE ALL WEAR HIS TROUSERS.

MINE SEEM TO FIT OKAY.

Uncle Fustas seemed fairly pleesed though...

THANK YOU FOR THOSE KIND WORDS, SIR! I TRUST THAT OUR...OUR TRAGIC LOSS WILL NOT AFFECT THE LONG STANDING GOOD RELATIONS WE'VE HAD WITH OUR JUDGES AND THAT WE CAN LOOK FORWARD TO MANY MORE HAPPY YEARS SUPPLYING YOU WITH TROUSERS.

SUPPOSE SO. NOT REALLY MY DEPARTMENT.

SCRIPT JOHN WAGNER
ART LIAM SHARP
LETTERING T FRAME

Get STUFFED at SARDINIE
WE'LL PUT HIM IN COMPANY RECEPTION. HE CAN GREET EVERY VISITOR WITH THAT FRIENDLY SMILE AND POSITIVE ATTITUDE THAT SAYS YESS! EMPHATICALLY YESS!
WILBUR GONE... JUST YOU LEFT NOW, WATT. AND MY DEAR NIECE MARGARET.

AND YOU, OF COURSE, MAYBE.
I SUPPOSE WE'LL NEED A NEW HEAD OF DESIGN... HOW D'YOU FEEL ABOUT TAKING ON THE TASK?
JUST GIVE ME THE CHANCE, MR YESS! I'LL SHOW YOU HOW A TROUSER DESIGN DEPARTMENT REALLY SHOULD BE – I MEAN...

I MEAN I'LL, UH... NEVER BE HALF THE TROUSER MAN WILBUR WAS, BUT I'LL DO MY LEVEL BEST FOR THE COMPANY, I PROMISE!

DON'T GET ANY IDEAS ABOVE YOUR STATION, MAYBE. YOU'RE STILL AN EMPLOYEE. YOU DON'T BECOME A **YESS** SIMPLY BY MARRYING INTO THE FAMILY. RIGHT, POP?
RIGHT, SON!

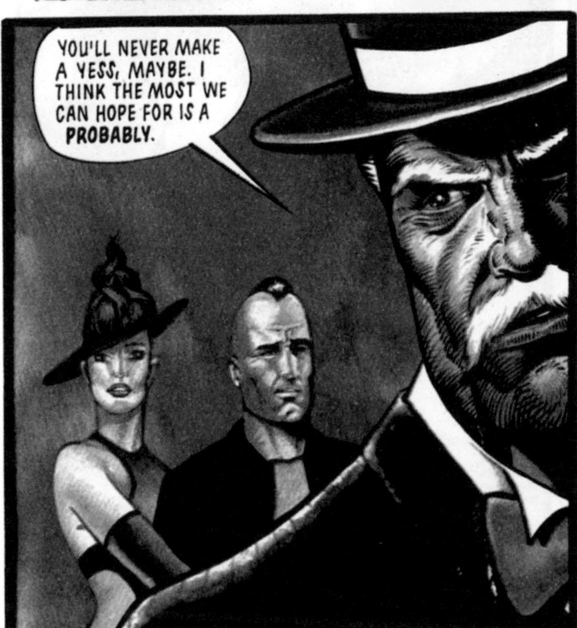
YOU'LL NEVER MAKE A YESS, MAYBE. I THINK THE MOST WE CAN HOPE FOR IS A **PROBABLY**.

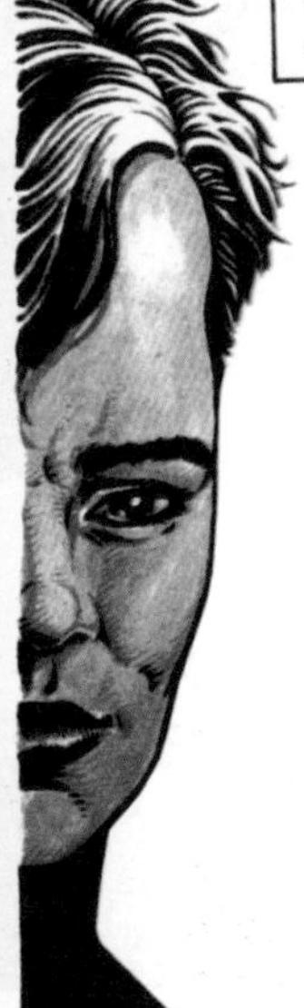
I decided to give Uncle Fusty a wek to get over his Loss before i disposed of cousin Watt.

JUDGE DREDD
JUDGE

On tuesDay I hung around the house and read Comics.
at leest, that's what my Ma was suposed to think. I didn't let her see the old volume on chemical synthesis. I'm supposed to be dumb.
Wedensday was Gastronella's party. I gave her a tatoo set. i loosened the spring on the needle pen so theres just a chance she'll do herself a nasty injry.
I wondered what she'd say if she knew id murdered 10 people. She'd probly think twice before using my tatoo set.
On friday me and Ma had a picknic in the block park. I let off a stink Bomb and we got kicked out. It was good cover for what I was up too with the chemistry set.
VACATE THE AREA, PLEASE. ODOUR LEVELS EXCEED THE NORM.
Over the weekend i completed the synthesis of the powerful hypnogenetic Id been working on.
It wasn't easy cos my equipment isnt up to much. i have to make do with what I can scrounge or steal from the school labs.
When we're rich i'll be able to afford the best.

On monday i went to the trowser factry where Dad works.
EMPHATICALLY YESS
DAD LEFT HIS LUNCH BEHIND. I BRUNG IT.
Cousin Wilbur was hard at work.
WILBUR YES! MODELS FOR YOU!
Dad was wearing his new three leg design.
TO HELL WITH WILBUR, P.J.! I'VE GONE AHEAD AND DONE IT! PRODUCTION STARTS TOMORROW!
I CALL THIS ONE "HARLEQUIN 3" – A LEG TO MATCH YOUR MOOD! LET IT ALL HANG LOOSE–
OR PERHAPS THE FREE LEG TUCKED INTO THE POCKET FOR THAT SUAVE MAN ABOUT TOWN LOOK.
WHAT DO YOU THINK, P.J.?
A NINE-DAY WONDER, DAD...
MAYBE EVEN TEN.
TEN! NOTHING LASTS THAT LONG!
STILL, WE CAN DREAM!
UNNFF!
TRIP!
STILL A FEW MINOR PROBLEMS TO BE IRONED OUT!
HMMM... PERHAPS A TUCK...?

And i popped in on cousin Watt...
BEAT IT, P.J., I'M BUSY.

HAVE SOME CANDY.
GET LOST, YOU LITTLE CREEP.
HAVE SOME CANDY AND I'LL TELL YOU ABOUT HOW DAD'S BEEN STEALING FROM THE COMPANY.

STEALING, EH? I KNEW IT! I KNEW WE COULDN'T TRUST THE BEGGAR! IN THE BLOOD, YOU KNOW. A MAYBE THROUGH AND THROUGH!
WELL – SPIT IT OUT!

The drug is called SLD 88. Shrinks used to use it on hopeless Loonies. It renders the Victim totally open to suggestion – leest that's wat the book says.
FIRST WHY DON'T YOU WRITE A SUICIDE NOTE?
WHAT?
OH, RIGHT! GOOD IDEA!

IT'S TO UNCLE FUSTER. PUT – DEAR DAD...
POP – I USUALLY CALL HIM POP.
GOOD POINT.

YOUR BROTHER'S DEATH HIT YOU MORE DEEPLY THAN YOU'VE SHOWN. YOU'VE ALWAYS KNOWN HE WAS THE BETTER SON. HE WAS SMARTER AND BETTER LOOKING AND, UH, MORE POSITIVE IN EVERY WAY. THE RESPONSIBILITY OF CARRYING ON THE YESS NAME IS TOO MUCH TO BEAR...
THIS IS GOOD STUFF!

OH, YES, AND PUT A PS – SAY YOU'VE CHANGED YOUR MIND ABOUT MY DAD. YOU THINK HE'S GOT THE DRIVE AND ABILITY TO GO ALL THE WAY.
ALL LIES, OF COURSE.
SURE, BUT USE IT.

HOW ABOUT "A MAN DESTINED TO BE BIG IN TROUSERS"...?
LIKE IT.

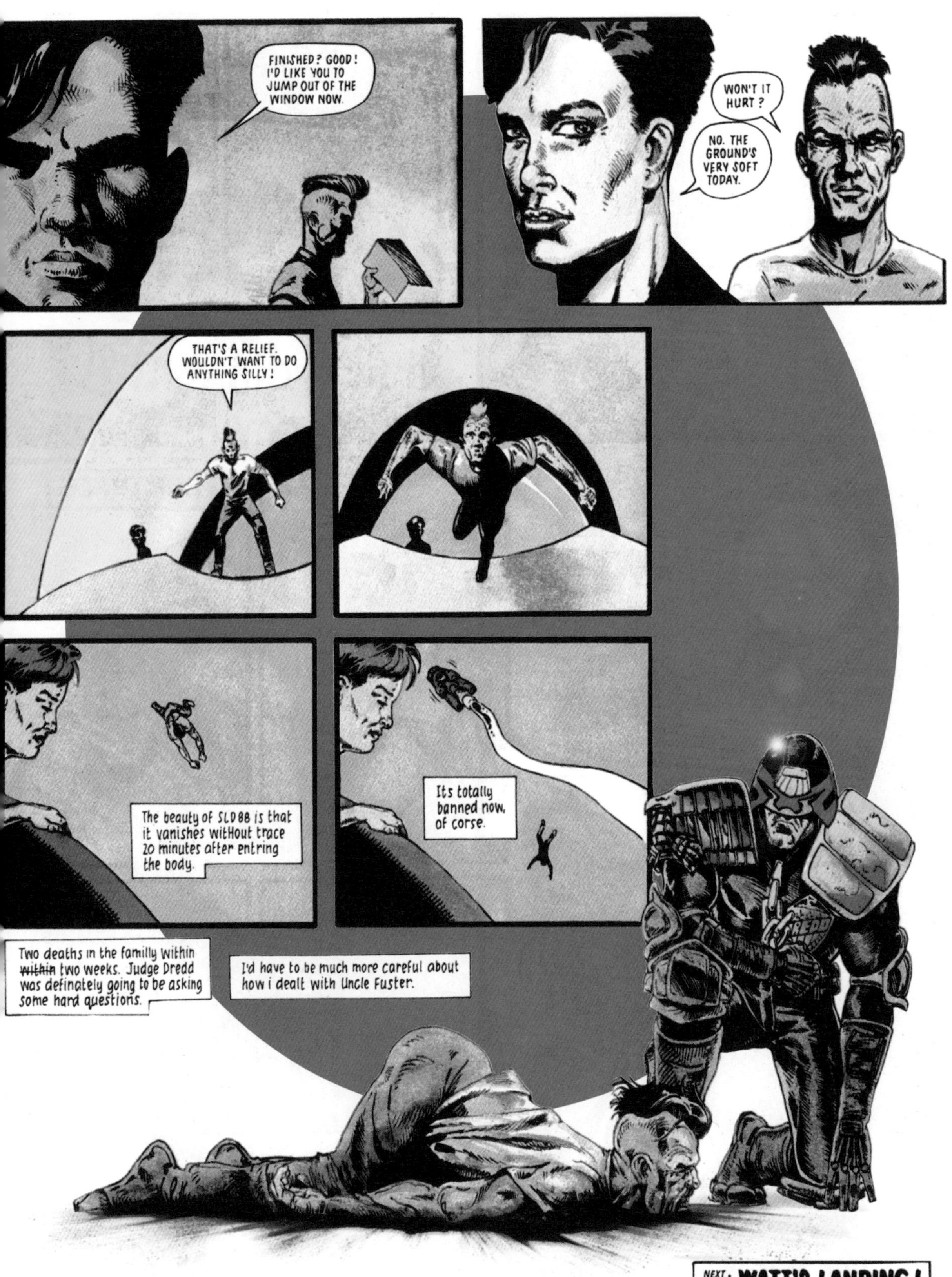
FINISHED? GOOD! I'D LIKE YOU TO JUMP OUT OF THE WINDOW NOW.
WON'T IT HURT?
NO. THE GROUND'S VERY SOFT TODAY.
THAT'S A RELIEF. WOULDN'T WANT TO DO ANYTHING SILLY!
The beauty of SLD88 is that it vanishes without trace 20 minutes after entring the body.
Its totally banned now, of corse.
Two deaths in the family within ~~within~~ two weeks. Judge Dredd was definately going to be asking some hard questions.
I'd have to be much more careful about how i dealt with Uncle Fuster.
NEXT PROG: WATT'S LANDING!

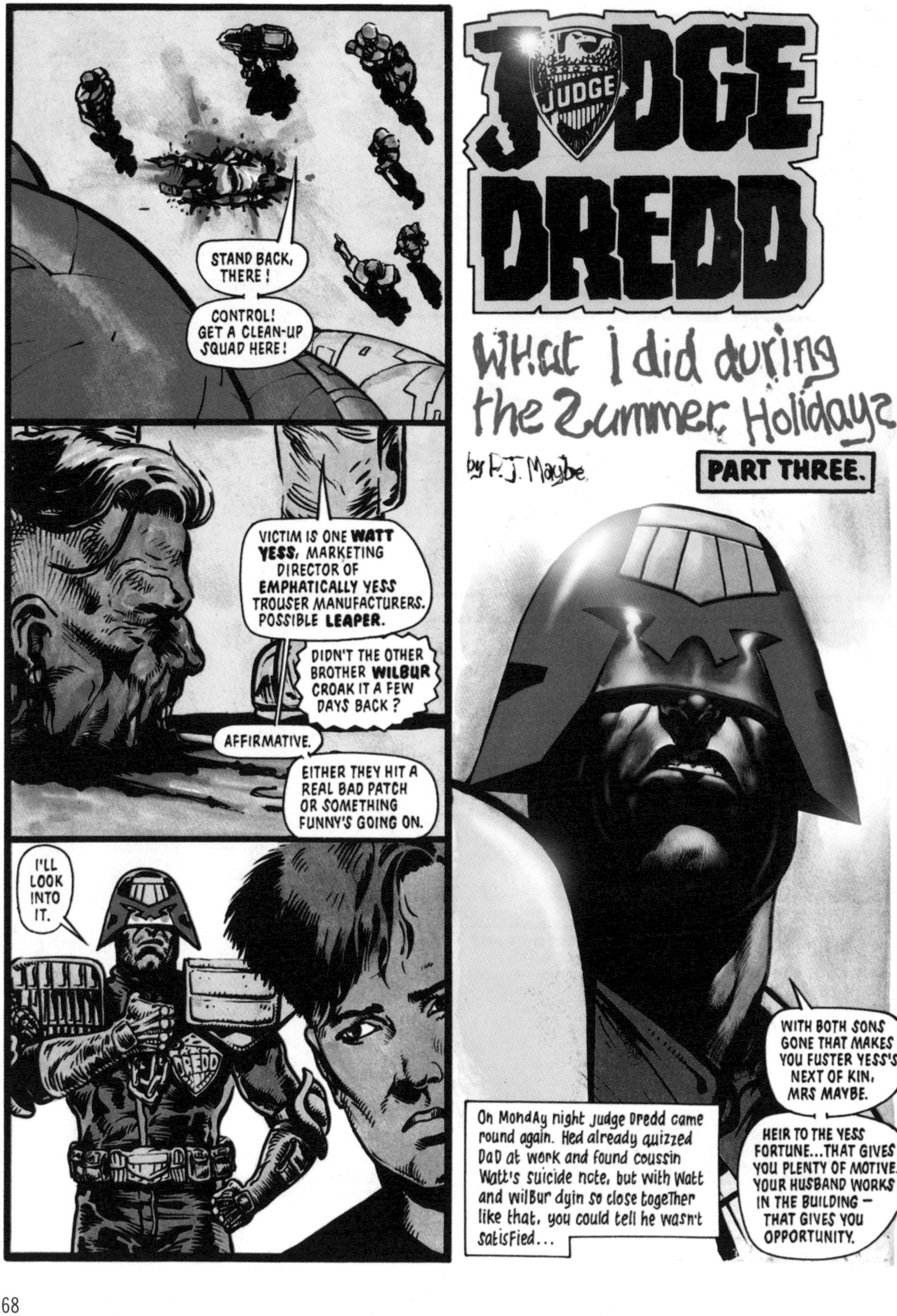

STAND BACK, THERE !
CONTROL! GET A CLEAN-UP SQUAD HERE!

VICTIM IS ONE **WATT YESS**, MARKETING DIRECTOR OF **EMPHATICALLY YESS** TROUSER MANUFACTURERS. POSSIBLE **LEAPER.**
DIDN'T THE OTHER BROTHER **WILBUR** CROAK IT A FEW DAYS BACK ?
AFFIRMATIVE.
EITHER THEY HIT A REAL BAD PATCH OR SOMETHING FUNNY'S GOING ON.

I'LL LOOK INTO IT.

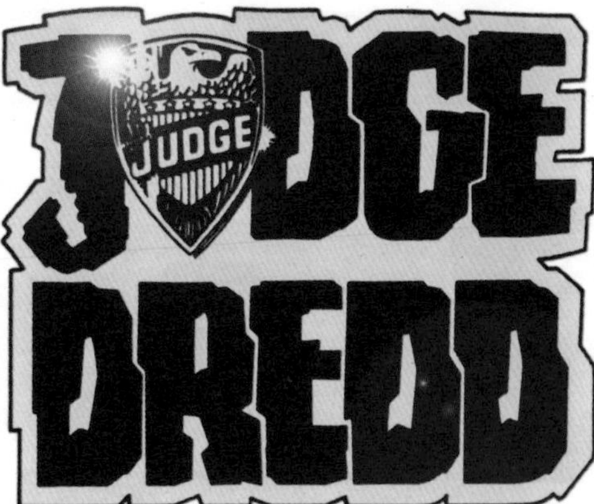

What I did during the Zummer Holidayz

by P.J. Maybe

PART THREE.

IF YOU'RE ACCUSING US OF SOMEHOW FAKING WATT'S SUICIDE YOU COULDN'T BE MORE WRONG! WE'RE NOT KILLERS!
Ma's story must've checked out on his Lie detector, but you could see it still niggled...
WHAT ABOUT YOU, SON? YOU KNOW ANYTHING YOU'RE NOT TELLING US?
I KNOW LOTSA THINGS.
CAT'S CRADLE!
YOU'LL HAVE TO EXCUSE P.J. HE... HE LIVES IN A WORLD OF HIS OWN.
SO I SEE.
WE'RE FAIRLY CERTAIN THE SUICIDE WAS GENUINE. DELAYED REACTION TO HIS BROTHER'S DEATH. IT'S QUITE COMMON. BUT WE HAVE TO CHECK THESE THINGS OUT.
SEE YOU AT THE STUFF SHOP.
SCRIPT JOHN WAGNER
ART LIAM SHARPE
LETTERING T FRAME

OH BOY! OH BOY! OH GLORY HALLELUJAH!
WE'RE IN THE MONEY...!
ROGER!
I HATE TO PROFIT FROM SOMEONE'S MISFORTUNE, HONEY – EVEN WATT AND WILBUR. BUT DON'T YOU SEE – WE'VE MADE IT! WE'RE HEIRS TO THE YESS FORTUNE! WE'RE GOING TO BE RICH!
SOMEBODY UP THERE MUST LIKE US!
On wendesday I went to visit my friend Gastronella in hospitle. that tatoo Pen i gave her had broke and cut her face pretty bad.
THIS IS ALL YOUR FAULT, P.J.!
I'M REALLY SORRY... HERE, I BRUNG THE RECEIPT.
I HEARD ABOUT A GUY GOT INJURED AND CLAIMED ON THE MANUFACTURERS. THEY PAID HIM 100,000 CREDS SHUT UP MONEY.
YOU DON'T SAY...
One of the lessuns I learnt really early is nothin oils the wheels as sweet as money.
WELL, EVERY CLOUD, AS THEY SAY...

It was really useful Gassy's accident happening so soon. cos there was a patient at the hospital sufferring from purple sore fever.
It's an infectious diseese spread by cursed Earth mites. Birds bring them in. It's kinda rare but anyone can get it.
It's really horrible. Victims take months to die, in Horrible Agony!
Best of all, there's no cure.
My Sience Project:
wednesday night I went round to Uncle Fusta's...
Uncle Fusty lives ina big place up on the hill. It's practically as big as our whole block and It's just for one old guy!
Plip!
Plip!

Ma'd been going round there lots just lately, to comfort him.
Plip!
Plip
Plip!
She said he'd taken to bed, under heavy sedation. He'd taken Watt and Wilbur's death real hard.
Plip!
Plip!
Plip!
Poor guy.
I used Bug on the Swindley's, but that was just a practise run. Since then I've added a remote control.
It took me ages to save up for it. that's the troubel about not having any money. Evrything's so hard to come buy.
Plip!
Plip!
Plip!
It was really great knowing that before long All this would be ours.

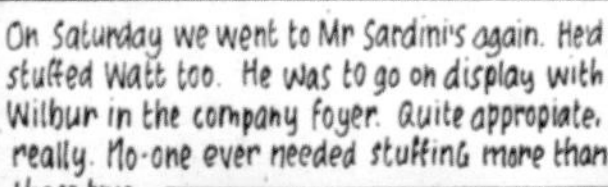
On Saturday we went to Mr Sardini's again. Hed stuffed Watt too. He was to go on display with Wilbur in the company foyer. Quite appropiate, really. No-one ever needed stuffing more than those two.

Judge Dredd was there again. Hed accepted Watt's death as suicide.
BAD LUCK, YESS. LET'S HOPE THIS IS THE END OF IT.
DREDD

I... I SUPPOSE THERE'S ONLY YOU NOW, MAYBE...
SAD, TSK!
EMPHATICALLY MAYBE... IT JUST DOESN'T SOUND RIGHT!

UNCLE FUSTER! ARE YOU ALL RIGHT...?
JUST... FELT A STAB OF PAIN, MY DEAR... IT'S NOTHING.

It'll be ages before the simptoms really start to show. Long Enough so the judgesdont start asking questions. And even if they do, who'd think of asking me ?
Pity about old fusty. Just his bad luck he happens to be rich – and related to me. Still, i'm sure if he knew he'd approve of my positive attitude.

Maybe I'm a true Yess after all.
P.J. – WHAT ARE YOU DOING?
AW, IT'S THIS DUMB ESSAY, MA – "WHAT I DID DURING THE SUMMER HOLIDAYS".

NO GOOD?
NAW!

NOTHIN' EVER SEEMS TO HAPPEN TO ME!
THE END... for now.

SCRIPT
JOHN WAGNER
ART
CARLOS EZQUERRA
LETTERS
ANNIE PARKHOUSE

Thanks to Robin Low.

JUDGE DREDD
ORIGINS

THE MISSION
LOGAN!
NO NEED TO SHOUT. I WAS JUST NEXT DOOR.
HERE'S A LIST.
Cohn
Venables
Waters
Renga
Ennerby
Sanchez
CHECK STATUS AND AVAILABILITY, ALL CURSED EARTH IMMUNISATIONS UP TO DATE, RATIONS FOR THIRTY DAYS. READY TO LEAVE AT 0600.
COHN... VENABLES... WATERS... RENGA...
I NEED EIGHT. COULD ONLY THINK OF SIX. BIT OUT OF TOUCH.
ENNERBY'S NO GO — CAUGHT A LOAD ON THAT SPEXER FIASCO.
OZMAN IS GOOD, HE'S AVAILABLE. YOU COULD TRY CURZON, JUST GRADUATED BUT HE'S SHARP. AND THERE'S ME.
YOU?
I KNOW THE HIP PLAYS ME UP, BUT IT'S JUST PAIN, THAT'S ALL. I ALWAYS GET OVERLOOKED FOR THE PLUMS.
HMM...
ALL RIGHT, LOGAN, BUT YOU BREAK DOWN YOU GO HOME ON YOUR OWN. YOU MAY FIND THIS IS NO PLUM.
COHN AND VENABLES ARE MED STAFF. YOU EXPECTING CASUALITIES THEN?
ALWAYS EXPECT. THAT WAY YOU WON'T BE DISAPPOINTED.

0530, WEST GATE NINE —
WE HAVE RECEIVED FROM PERSONS UNKNOWN A RANSOM DEMAND FOR THE RETURN OF THE BODY OF JUDGE EUSTACE FARGO.
IT'S MISSING?
HIS TOMB'S IN THE HALL OF JUSTICE. I PASSED IT ONLY YESTERDAY.
HOW COULD ANYONE GET TO IT THERE?
THEY DIDN'T HAVE TO. I HAVE SOME INFORMATION FOR YOU, AND THIS GOES NO FURTHER THAN THIS ROOM —
JUDGE FARGO HAS NEVER BEEN IN THAT TOMB.
YOU'RE KIDDING. BUT WE WERE ALWAYS TOLD —
FABRICATED.
FARGO'S BODY WAS... SHALL WE SAY, MISAPPROPRIATED. UNTIL NOW WE HAD THOUGHT IT LOST FOREVER.
IT SEEMS NOT.

ONE BILLION CREDITS.
THAT WAS THE DEMAND. ALL USED, ALL IMPOSSIBLE TO TRACE.
THAT'S SERIOUS MONEY...
YOU DON'T THINK IT OUGHT TO BE IN SOMETHING MORE SECURE? A FEW HEAVY LASERS AT LEAST?
THAT WAS ALSO PART OF THE TERMS — AND JUST ENOUGH OF US TO DEFEND IT FROM RANDOM ATTACK.
WE HAVE BEEN GIVEN A ROUTE. WE WILL RECEIVE FURTHER INSTRUCTIONS ALONG THE WAY. WHOEVER THEY ARE, THEY'RE TAKING NO CHANCES.
PARDON ME SAYING IT, BUT IT'S A LOT OF DANGER AND EXPENSE TO GO TO OVER A DEAD MAN.
C'MON, WATERS, FARGO'S THE FATHER OF JUSTICE — YOU CAN'T LEAVE HIS BODY IN CRIMINAL HANDS.
HOW DO WE KNOW THEY'VE GOT THE BODY ANYWAY?
WE HAVE... A CERTAIN AMOUNT OF PHYSICAL EVIDENCE.

SOME 'DULT GIMME FIFTY CREDS TO GIVE YA THIS.
WHAT-?
DOWN! EVERYBODY DOWN!
HUH?
HASN'T GONE OFF -!
GET BACK, KID!
FRONT DESK! WE HAVE A SUSPECTED EXPLOSIVE DEVICE!
THE INNER CONTAINER WAS REFRIGERATED. IT HELD A SECTION OF HUMAN TISSUE. ITS DNA WAS IDENTICAL TO YOURS.
THIS CAME WITH IT.
YOU DON'T SEEM SURPRISED.
Fargo
Price for remainder one billion credits used currency only.
Funds leave Mega-City One tomorrow A.M., route specified below. Further instructions will be given en route.
Small escort only, no heavy armament.
No tricks.
LET'S SAY I HAD A SUSPICION FARGO MIGHT BE INVOLVED.
SO GANT PASSED THE BOX TO THE JUVE FOR DELIVERY.* AND YOU THINK IT'S MY CLONE-FATHER?
IT'S HIGHLY PROBABLE.
*THARGNOTE: SEE PROG 1504.

THE AGE AND LEVELS OF ABSORBED CONTAMINANTS INDICATE A MAN WHO LIVED THROUGH MOST OF THE LAST CENTURY — AND THAT'S IMPOSSIBLE TO FAKE.
AND THERE'S ONE OTHER THING YOU SHOULD KNOW...
THE TISSUE WAS FRESH, DREDD, TAKEN FROM A **LIVING** ORGANISM.
JUDGE FARGO — IF INDEED IT IS FARGO — MAY STILL BE **ALIVE!**

THEY PRESS ON THROUGH THAT DESOLATE WASTELAND LITTERED WITH THE REMNANTS OF A LIFE THAT ONCE HAD BEEN —
JUDGE DREDD
ORIGINS
PART 2 LEGACY
SCRIPT JOHN WAGNER
ART CARLOS EZQUERRA
LETTERS ANNIE PARKHOUSE
— RUSTING, CRUMBLING MEMORIALS TO THE LAND THEY CALLED AMERICA.
Open 24 Hours
HERE AND THERE SETTLEMENTS HAVE GROWN UP AMONG THE RUINS —
— THE CHILDREN OF THE APOCALYPSE, MADE WORN AND TWISTED AND BITTER BY THE HARSHNESS OF THE CURSED EARTH.
THEY GAVE THEM WIDE BERTH.
RIDE ON.

THIS TORTURED LAND...
NOT FARGO'S LEGACY, AS MANY THOUGHT, BUT DEMOCRACY'S — A PRODUCT OF THE CORRUPTION THE JUDGES HAD BEEN FORMED TO FIGHT.
IN THAT RESPECT AT LEAST, THEY HAD FAILED. TOO LATE. TOO LATE TO PREVENT DISASTER...
WHEN DO YOU RECKON THEY'LL MAKE CONTACT?
NOT TODAY. NOT FOR A WHILE. THEY WANT US WELL AWAY FROM THE CITY.
SOMETHING BURNING UP AHEAD.
LOOKS LIKE A RADWAGON.
MUTANT. ONE OF THE ATTACKERS. THAT'S HOME-MADE ARMOUR.
WOMAN'S DEAD. SHOT UP LIKE A PRACTICE DROID.
THE BUH...THE BABY. TH-THEY GOT THE BABY...

GUH... GOT SEPARATED FROM...FROM THE 'TREK. BIG DAMN MISTAKE...
SAVE HIM. DON'T LET THEM...HAVE MY...LITTLE BOY...
SO MUCH FOR THEIR NEW LIFE.
YOU GOTTA ASK, THE CITY WAS THIS BAD?
TRACKS EVERYWHERE. THESE ONES LOOK THE FRESHEST — HEADING INTO THE HILLS.
NOT OUR BUSINESS, RENGA. WE'VE GOT OUR INSTRUCTIONS.
DREDD TO JUSTICE WATCH. COME IN. ARE YOU READING ME?
NOTHING. TOO MUCH INTERFERENCE.
VZZZZT ZZZT
BRZZZZ
SO IT'S JUST US. WE'VE GOT TO DO SOMETHING. WE CAN'T LEAVE THAT BABY TO THE MUTIES.
I AGREE. I MEAN, WHAT'S SOME DEAD OLD BONES TO A JUVEY'S LIFE?
GOT TO SAY IT, DREDD. FATHER OF JUSTICE, SURE, BUT HE'S STILL OLD BONES. THAT LITTLE BOY COULD STILL BE ALIVE.
ALL RIGHT. CURZON, SANCHEZ, RENGA, YOU COME WITH ME. WATERS, YOU'RE IN CHARGE HERE.
FIND SOME DEFENSIBLE GROUND. WHOEVER DID THIS MAY BE BACK.
CHECK.

DREDD'S PARTY HAS SET OFF THROUGH THE CURSED EARTH TO RECLAIM THE BODY OF JUDGE FARGO, HELD BY PERSONS UNKNOWN. FOLLOWING DIRECTIONS LAID DOWN FOR THEM, THEY REACH A TRADING POST —
TRADING POST
YOU HAVE A MESSAGE FOR ME?
MEGA-CITY JUDGE, HUH? RECKON I MIGHT.
THEY SAID YOU'D GIVE ME FIFTY CREDS.
WHO'S THEY?
COUPLE OF GUYS, DROPPED IN ON A HOVERSKIMMER THREE DAYS AGO. FACES ALL WRAPPED UP LIKE THEY DIDN'T WANT TO BE RECOGNISED.
HMMPH.
SCRIPT JOHN WAGNER
ART CARLOS EZQUERRA
LETTERS ANNIE PARKHOUSE
ROUTE MAP. CREEPS AREN'T READY TO MAKE CONTACT YET.
KEEP RIDING WE'LL BE WATCHING
TRADING POST
CAMP, THAT NIGHT —
HAVE TO MAKE A LITTLE DETOUR, WATERS. I'LL TAKE LOGAN AND COHN WITH ME.
IN THE MORNING MOVE ON. WAIT FOR US HERE, AT THE RIVER CROSSING.
YOU THINK IT'S WISE, SPLITTING UP AGAIN?
JUDGE DREDD ORIGINS
PART 6 FARGOVILLE
RATHER AVOID IT, BUT THERE'S SOMETHING I NEED TO CHECK OUT.
SIGNALS ARE COMING THROUGH AGAIN. STAY IN CONTACT WITH AERIAL UNITS. ANY TROUBLE, CALL THEM IN.
NO CHANCE OF A LITTLE SLEEP, SIR? I'M PRETTY BUSHED.
"SLEEP IN THE SADDLE, COHN. TIME'S PRESSING."

MORNING —
RIDERS COMIN', BOSS!
I SAY YOU COULD TALK, BOY?
SOME O' THESE BOYS STILL GOTTA LEARN THE RULES! TAKE HIM TO THE HOTBOX!
NO! NOT THAT! I'M SORRY! I WON'T TALK AGAIN!
YOU'RE TALKIN' NOW, BOY!
DAMNED IF THEY DON'T LOOK LIKE BIG-CITY JUDGES. BETTER GO WARN THE TOWN.
YESSIR!
FARGOVILLE
BIRTHPLACE OF JUDGE EUSTACE FARGO
FARGO'S BIRTHPLACE!
FUNNY, NEVER THOUGHT OF HIM BEING BORN — LIKE NATURAL, I MEAN.

NO GUNS IN FARGOVILLE
NO LUDE OR RIOTOUS
NO SPITTING SWEARING NAME-CALLING
NO EYEING UP OUR WIMMEN
LOOKS LIKE THEY CAUGHT THE LAW BUG REAL BAD.
KEEP YOUR EYES OPEN AND YOUR WEAPONS READY. NO TELLING WHAT KIND OF RECEPTION WE'RE GOING TO GET.
PAPUM
PAPUM
PUM
PUMRUM
WELCOME, WELCOME FRIENDS!
I'M MAYOR EUSTACE BLUNT! THIS HERE'S SHERIFF EUSTACE GARVIE!
MAY I SAY WHAT A TRUE PLEASURE IT IS TO RECEIVE THE DISCIPLES OF EUSTACE FARGO BACK IN HIS BIRTHPLACE, THE TRUE CRADLE OF LAW IN THIS MODERN AGE!
DIDN'T EXPECT A MARCHING BAND. STILL, SURE BEATS A GUNFIGHT.

SINCE THE DEVASTATION OF AMERICA WE ALONE HAVE KEPT THE TORCH OF JUSTICE BURNIN' IN THESE PARTS, A BASTION OF NORMALITY AMONG THE MUTANT HORDES!
HERE IN FARGOVILLE I AM PROUD TO SAY A CRIME IS STILL A CRIME AND NO CRIME EVER GOES UNPUNISHED!
'FACT, WE WERE JUST FIXIN' TO HANG US SOME MUTIES! YOU CAN BE GUESTS OF HONOUR!
THANKS, BUT WE'LL PASS.
A KIND OF MADNESS INFECTS THIS TOWN, BUT IT'S NOT OUR BUSINESS TO INTERFERE...
HERE, LOOK AT HIM! LOOK AT THAT CHIN! HE COULD BE EUSTACE FARGO HISSELF!
OOOHHH!
IT'S UNCANNY!
MY NAME IS DREDD. I AM A CLONE GROWN FROM THE GENETIC MATERIAL OF FARGO. IN MANY WAYS YOU COULD SAY I AM EUSTACE FARGO.
WHEE-EE! FARGO HISSELF BACK FROM THE DEAD!
AIN'T THAT A TURN UP!
WE'RE HERE TO ASK FOR YOUR HELP. THERE ARE DETAILS OF FARGO'S LIFE I MUST LOOK INTO.
SURE THING! EVERYTHING YOU COULD EVER WANT TO KNOW, IT'S ALL THERE IN OUR OWN LITTLE MUSEUM!
YOU GO RIGHT IN, FELLAS! I'M GIVIN' YOU FREE PASSES FOR LIFE!
THEY SURE LIKE FARGO. PLACE IS LIKE A SHRINE.
YEAH. YOU FIGURE THERE'S ANYONE IN TOWN WHO'S NOT CALLED EUSTACE?
STEP RIGHT IN, FOLKS! I'M EUSTACE JOHNSON, MUSEUM CURATOR. ANYTHIN' YOU WANNA KNOW, JUST ASK.
LET THERE BE JUST FOR A

GOT A WHOLE SELECTION OF HIS BIKES, RIGHT FROM WHEN HE WAS A LITTLE BITTY KIDDIE.
MAN, A **LAWRANGER**! THAT WAS THE **PROTOTYPE** FOR THE LAWMASTER. LOOK AT THE ARMAMENT — RIGHT OUT OF THE DARK AGES.
THEY WERE PRONE TO JAMMING. HELD 200 ROUNDS, BLUNTNOSE .45S.
YOU SURE KNOW YOUR STUFF, YOUNG MAN.
THIS HERE WAS HIS FIRST BB GUN, GIVEN TO LITTLE EUSTACE FOR HIS FIFTH BIRTHDAY. BY THE TIME HE WAS **SIX** HE WAS A **DEAD SHOT**. USED TO ROAM THE COUNTRYSIDE, SHOOTIN' PRACTICALLY ANYTHIN' THAT **MOVED**.
AND HERE WE HAVE HIS MAMMY AN' PAPPY, **NATHAN** AN' **MARY**. NATHAN WAS **CIRCUIT JUDGE** ROUND THESE PARTS, AN' HE INSTILLED IN THE BOY A LOVE OF JUSTICE AN' FAIR PLAY.
MARY WAS A KINDLY WOMAN, BUT STRICT. NOT EXACTLY CHURCHY, IF YOU KNOW WHAT I MEAN, BUT SHE WOULDN'T PUT UP WITH NO NONSENSE FROM THE BOY.
NEVER SAW A PICTURE OF THEM BEFORE. TOO MUCH OF THE ARCHIVE WAS DESTROYED IN THE WAR.
HIS PARENTS... **MY** PARENTS. APART FROM RICO, THE NEAREST THING I HAVE TO A FAMILY.
SIT DOWN, SIT DOWN, FOLKS. WE GOT A WHOLE FILM SHOW HERE. YOU MIGHT AS WELL SEE THINGS RIGHT FROM THE BEGINNING.
JUST MAKE YOURSELVES COMFORTABLE AN' I'LL GO GET HER STARTED.
THE YEAR IS 1999. AT 20.45 ON THE NIGHT OF JANUARY 9, AT 16 MAIN STREET IN THE TOWN OF JAXVILLE, A HAPPY EVENT IS TAKING PLACE.
JAXVILLE?
THEY CHANGED THE NAME TO FARGOVILLE AFTER HIS DEATH, I KNOW THAT MUCH.

 That's it for our Origins extract. Pick up the story in Rebellion's *ORIGINS*.